"Finished, is it?"

The vibration in his voice was like the guttural warning of a jungle cat about to attack. Before she had time to move, her wrist was caught in a vice-like grip, as his sensuous mouth crushed hers in brutal, dominating savagery.

She was captive in his arms, for even his cruelty drew her, his magnetism far too strong. . . . She found herself swept irresistably into the maelstrom of an all-consuming passion equal to his own. . . .

At last, breathing heavily, he held her from him, a sneering lift of triumph to his mouth as he saw the dark and dreamy glaze that covered her eyes.

"Well, Karen," he said in some amusement, "it wasn't finished, was it? But it is now, because I say so. . . ."

ANNE HAMPSON
has the same impetuous streak as her heroines. It often lands her in the middle of a new country, a new adventure—and a new book. Her first-hand knowledge of her settings and her lively characters have combined to delight her readers throughout the world.

Dear Reader:

Silhouette Romances is an exciting new publishing venture. We will be presenting the very finest writers of contemporary romantic fiction as well as outstanding new talent in this field. It is our hope that our stories, our heroes and our heroines will give you, the reader, all you want from romantic fiction.

Also, *you* play an important part in our future plans for Silhouette Romances. We welcome any suggestions or comments on our books and I invite you to write to us at the address below.

So, enjoy this book and all the wonderful romances from Silhouette. They're for *you*!

Karen Solem
Editor-in-Chief
Silhouette Books
P.O. Box 769
New York, N.Y. 10019

ANNE HAMPSON

Stormy Masquerade

Published by Silhouette Books New York

America's Publisher of Contemporary Romance

Other Silhouette Romances by Anne Hampson

Payment in Full
The Dawn Steals Softly
Second Tomorrow
Man of the Outback
Where Eagles Nest

SILHOUETTE BOOKS, a Simon & Schuster Division of
GULF & WESTERN CORPORATION
1230 Avenue of the Americas, New York, N.Y. 10020

Distributed by Pocket Books

ISBN: 0-671-57004-8

First Silhouette printing May, 1980

10 9 8 7 6 5 4 3

America's Publisher of Contemporary Romance

Printed in the U.S.A.

Chapter One

The curtain fell to a deafening round of applause from a loyal and enthusiastic audience. It was another triumph for the Parkside Amateur Dramatic Society, and especially for Karen Waring and her friend Meryl Dempster.

'Just listen to that!' Automatically Meryl flicked a hand toward the lowered curtain. 'Gratifying, isn't it?'

Karen nodded, but before she had time to say anything the curtain was rising again and the entire cast was bowing to the audience.

'You were marvelous, as usual,' Karen was saying a few minutes later when they were in the dressing room they shared. 'If you're serious about making acting your career you'll be a star one day.' Having removed a long sleeky blond wig, Karen was busy taking off the makeup which added over ten years to her age. 'Most of the applause was for you,' she added sincerely. 'The author of the play would be delighted with your performance if only he could see it.'

'Thank you,' murmured Meryl from her place at the other dressing table. 'But, Karen, you know very well that you are just as popular with our supporters as I. They loved your performance.'

'I little thought,' mused Karen, 'when I let you persuade me to join the company, that I'd ever be anything more than an extra, yet here I am, the bitch par excellence!' She turned her dark head and laughed. 'No wonder I never find a boy friend!'

'Don't you ever get fed up with being the nasty piece of work all the time?' Meryl was dabbing her face with a pad of cotton wool soaked in *eau de Cologne*. 'I'm sure I should.'

'No; I enjoy the role I slipped into. Maybe I'm basically the bitchy type of girl and that's the secret of my success.'

'Hello . . . fishing for compliments,' teased Meryl, and they both laughed.

However, a frown soon appeared on Karen's brow, and her big gray-green eyes were shadowed. Meryl, noticing the change as she caught her friend's expression through the mirror, swiveled round on her stool to ask anxiously what was wrong.

'I'm restless,' admitted Karen with a little impatient sigh. 'I'm undecided about staying with Brown and Forsythe when my boss retires. I've been told that it's almost a certainty that I shall have to go to John Lacey, whose secretary's leaving to get married.'

Meryl grimaced.

'He's not a nice man, from what you've told me.'

'No one likes him. He's surly, bad-tempered and faultfinding. Dorothy told me she wouldn't have stuck it out this long if she hadn't been getting married and knew she'd be leaving soon. She's been a saint to put up with him as long as she has.'

'Are jobs easy to get?' asked Meryl, troubled.

'I don't really know. But in any case, I've had itchy feet ever since my sister got that job in Barbados. As you know, she works as a receptionist in an hotel. I wish I could land a job that would take me abroad.' Karen shrugged her shoulders resignedly. 'I'd never be as lucky as Jean. She got to know the manager of the Vervain Hotel when he was in London. He was staying at the hotel where she worked. Before he left he asked her if she'd be interested in working for him, on the island of Barbados. Naturally she jumped at the chance since, like me, she's no ties.'

Meryl nodded. Having finished removing her makeup she rose from the stool and stood for a moment looking at her friend through the mirror, noting the rare, classical beauty of her features—the high cheekbones with the transparent, alabaster skin stretched tightly over them, those unusual widely spaced eyes that always seemed to have a dewy look about them, the full, generous mouth and firm, pointed chin which gave her face an oval shape. Her hair, mid-brown touched with tawny-gold, was long and straight, flicked up at the ends and with a half-fringe falling enchantingly on to the high, intelligent forehead. Meryl's own beauty was fair and deceptively fragile; Karen's was of a darker, stronger kind which, to Meryl, seemed to possess the sort of delightful witchery that would appeal to any man. And yet, at twenty-two, Karen had not yet become interested enough in the opposite sex to offer encouragement to any of those men who, at various times, would have liked to go steady with her.

She had taken off the last of the heavy makeup and Meryl could not help but compare this unsophisticated beauty with what Karen had been like only twenty minutes ago. The bitch par excellence was no understatement!

'You fascinate me the way you make yourself up so expertly.' Meryl was thinking about George, their special makeup man who had been somewhat resentful when Karen decided to try doing it herself. But he had since admitted that Karen was a master hand. 'There's no doubt,' went on Meryl, speaking her thoughts aloud, 'that if you wanted to disguise yourself you'd have no difficulty at all. I'm sure you could deceive anyone—even me—if you wanted to.'

Karen laughed, recalling her first attempts, one evening when George was pushed for time, having arrived late owing to his car breaking down. To her own surprise she had been more than satisfied with her attempts and, with the practice she had had since, she mentally agreed that she would have no trouble in adopting an efficient disguise.

'I don't know about deceiving you,' she returned doubtfully. 'And as I've no criminal leanings I can't imagine a situation where I'd want to disguise myself.'

But how little she knew . . .

When, a week later, the final curtain came down on Clint Fraser's play, *One Stolen Hour*, there was not one among the cast who was not keyed up with anticipation, for the playwright had not only been in the audience, but he was to attend the party at the Sandiway Hotel which the company was throwing afterward, as this was the final week of the present season.

'I never imagined I'd ever have the honour of meeting the famous Clint Fraser!' Phil Armstrong had exclaimed a few days previously when the cast had been told that the author was to do them the honour of attending the last performance. Phil played the lead, mostly, and he, like Meryl, was keen to make acting a career. 'I wonder if he's coming as a scout?'

'He'd not bother his head about anything like that,' returned Leonard Holt, who had taken the part of the villain in the play. 'It's just interest, I expect, to see what a mess the amateurs can make of his play.'

Karen had said nothing; she had seen the playwright interviewed on television, and while admitting that his looks were extraordinarily attractive, and that there was something strikingly powerful and arresting about his tall, immaculately clad figure, she had found herself denouncing him as an arrogant, conceited man who was far too conscious of his position as one of the world's most talented playwrights.

However, on hearing that he was willing to come to a small theatre to see amateurs performing his play, and then to attend their party afterward, Karen was ready to revise her opinion of him and begin all over again.

As the cast was not changing until after the party, it was as the sleeky, blond-haired villainess that Karen was introduced to Clint Fraser by Jake Sheridan, their producer.

'How do you do?' Clint's handshake hurt; his pewter-gray eyes below straight black brows seemed to look through her rather than at her, and she knew for sure that he had not even taken the trouble to memorize her name. She colored when his eyes moved, to make a cursory examination of the sexy svelte figure revealed by the slinky satin dress she wore. She was glad to move away to allow Jake to introduce Meryl.

'He's a real he-man!' Meryl was exclaiming later when she and Karen were at the buffet table, plates in hands. 'And did you notice how handsome he is? And that attractive quality in his voice—stern, sort of, and yet you had the impression that he could be very kind. Did *you* notice that tone in his voice, Karen?'

'I noticed his arrogance,' was Karen's sardonic rejoinder as she helped herself to a slice of chicken from a dish. 'He's full of his own importance, if you ask me.'

Meryl laughed, her blue eyes alight.

'Your opinion of him matches that of most of the females in the cast. He seems not to be interested. But me—' She broke off and wagged a teasing forefinger. 'I, my bitchy one, am different! He congratulated me on my performance and said the kindest thing!'

'Good for you,' she said sarcastically as Karen stabbed a piece of meat pie with her fork. 'And what was this eloquent and flattering distinction he accorded you?'

Meryl laughed heartily.

'Don't be catty! And you're not on the stage now so you needn't speak like that! He said I ought to make acting my career.'

Karen swung around, sincerely interested now.

'He did? I'm so glad, Meryl. You're going to take his advice?'

'I think so, but later. Mum needs my money at present, just until the twins leave school and start work. If only Dad hadn't gone off and left us. . . .' Her voice trailed, and silence fell between the two girls, each busy with her own thoughts—Meryl dwelling on the misfortune that had befallen her family when her father went off with a girl of nineteen, and Karen reflecting on the untimely death of her parents in a railway accident four years ago, when Karen and her sister were left with no one else in the world.

'I'm getting morbid!' declared Meryl, and instantly became herself again. 'Gosh, I'm ready for this food! Where shall we sit?'

'Here,' from Josie Barlow who was with two other members of the company. 'We can easily make room at our table.'

The five chatted while they ate and then Karen and Meryl were alone again as the other three moved off. But they were soon joined by Phil, to whom Meryl said instantly, 'I saw you talking to our star guest.' She looked at him questioningly, wanting to learn something about the playwright.

'He was saying he's writing his next play on a boat. Jake was telling me earlier that he has a fabulous luxury cabin cruiser which he's going to moor at Barbados. He's going there in a fortnight or three weeks time. Jake asked how long the play would take to write and he said about six months. Imagine having six months in the Caribbean! I wish I could write plays!'

Karen glanced toward the man being discussed. Lean of build and strikingly handsome, he possessed the unmistakable attributes of culture and good breeding. His confidence obviously stemmed from the success of achievement; his air of distinction marked him an aristocrat, and Karen recalled that in the television interview it was revealed that he was connected with one of the most noble families in the country. He was in conversation with Jake, whose entire interest he was holding, when Sylvia Dawson, one of the cast, intruded into the conversation, and Karen saw that Clint hardly glanced at her before turning his head and resuming his discourse with the producer. Karen set her mouth, wishing she had the opportunity of telling him what she thought of his rudeness.

'Barbados?' Meryl's voice broke into Karen's train of thought and she put the objectionable Clint Fraser from her mind. 'Karen's sister lives there.'

'Yes, I know. Karen told me.' Phil continued to talk about the playwright for a few minutes, then looked up to see Jake approaching their table.

'And how do you like our Mr. Fraser?' Jake spoke pleasantly, his smile a little reserved. He was a thin, balding man with polished manners that always seemed at variance with the casual way he dressed, usually in denims and a roll-neck sweater. 'A charming fellow, don't you think?'

Meryl nodded but laughed as she saw her friend's expression.

'I like him well enough,' she said, 'but Karen wasn't all that impressed.'

'He's rather aloof at times.' Jake glanced around and

added, 'Let me get myself a few eats and I'll be right back.'

'Phil says he's writing his next play on a boat,' said Meryl when Jake returned and took a seat at the table.

'Where is his home?' Karen was trying to remember if it had been mentioned in the television interview.

'On the island of Grenada—the Spice Island.'

'But he's going to live on his boat? I wonder why?'

'He was saying that it's an experiment because he wants to get right away from everyone—servants, friends, the lot. He'll have almost total isolation on his boat.'

Karen became thoughtful, wondering how far Clint's boat would be from the hotel in which her sister worked.

'You're not your usual bright self,' observed Jake on suddenly noticing Karen's serious expression. 'Anything wrong?'

'It's nothing,' she said, and would have changed the subject but Meryl broke in to say, 'Karen's not happy about her job. As you know, her boss is leaving and she might have to work for a man she doesn't like.'

'I might try for a job that involves travel,' mused Karen.

Jake's eyes flickered over her.

'If you'd been older you could have had a job on Clint Fraser's boat.'

'I could?' Karen's eyes automatically slid to the man in question. His gaze met hers, stony and indifferent before he glanced away again. 'What doing?' Karen added without much interest. 'You just said he wanted to be alone.'

'He needs a woman to do for him. A sort of Girl Friday, from what I gather.'

'A Girl Friday,' from Meryl interestedly. 'Why must she be older?'

'I suspect it's because the young ones forget the real reason why they're there,' laughed Jake.

'You mean—?' began Karen, then stopped, colouring slightly.

'Yes, that's what I mean. A handsome man on a boat with a pretty girl—and the romantic setting of the Caribbean. . . . Well, I ask you?'

'He actually said that girls run after him?' Karen's eyes reflected contempt, but Jake was shaking his head even before her last word was out.

'Not at all, Karen. Don't be bitchy offstage,' he admonished with a mock severity. 'I gathered this myself—I'm very astute you know,' he added laughing. 'But he did say that he was having someone older because he was intending to write, not to pander to the whims of some female avid for romance.'

Karen gasped.

'The pompous, opinionated creature!' she exclaimed. 'Some female ought to teach him a lesson!'

Jake merely shrugged and laughed.

'How old has this woman to be?' Meryl wanted to know, her fork poised half-way to her mouth.

'Over forty-five. He's advertising in the newspapers sometime this week—at least, I think that was what he said.'

'I doubt if a woman over forty-five would want to be a Girl Friday,' said Karen. 'What are the duties?'

'He wants someone to cook and clean, and to wash

his clothes. He wasn't all that communicative,' Jake went on to add, a faintly bored note creeping into his voice, as if he were no longer interested in the subject. 'The woman will have a great deal of time off, from what I can gather.'

He left soon afterward and to Karen's surprise the playwright sauntered over to them. His movements were languid, with an almost uncanny grace about them that could not fail to attract attention. Karen noticed that several pairs of feminine eyes were following him as he crossed the room.

'May I join you?' Polite the voice, finely modulated and cultured. 'The heroine and villainess, eh?' He threw Karen a cursory glance before giving his whole attention to Meryl. She wore a little makeup, so that her prettiness came through, whereas Karen was heavily made up; as the bitch in the play she was thirty-five years of age and, therefore, totally different in appearance from her natural self.

'We thoroughly enjoyed acting in your play,' Meryl was saying enthusiastically, appearing to be perfectly at her ease with the man who, leaning back in his chair, was idly tapping the arm; and to Karen's critical mind even this small movement was irritating, because she regarded it as a sign of arrogance. 'Did you enjoy writing it, Mr. Fraser?'

'Yes, I enjoy all my plays.'

'All?' interposed Karen in surprise. 'You never write one you have difficulty with?'

'We weren't speaking of difficulty—' He paused as if trying to recall her name. Karen merely waited, determinedly refraining from offering it. 'We were speaking of enjoyment. Naturally I sometimes have difficulty, but I still enjoy writing the plays. If I found I wasn't enjoying a play then I'd scrap it at once, because it's my firm conviciton that anything which becomes a chore is bound to be inferior on completion.'

'There's a great deal of logic in that,' Karen was forced to admit, albeit grudgingly. Clint's pewter-gray eyes were cynical and it was patently clear that he had guessed she had made the admission reluctantly.

After staying with them—talking mainly to Meryl—he moved on. Meryl turned to Karen, eyeing her curiously.

'You were using your bitchy voice,' she said. 'Why?'

Karen shrugged. She could not have answered the question because she did not know what had prompted her to use the husky, sexy voice she had used on stage.

'It was good enough for him,' was all she said and was relieved when Meryl merely laughed and changed the subject.

'I think we ought to be socialising,' Meryl said after a while and Karen nodded in agreement. But she was finding the room stifling and after a few minutes she went outside for a breath of fresh air.

She was sitting on a dimly lit patio when Clint Fraser came out and she shrank back instinctively but realised he had seen her. She stood up without knowing why. He did not speak and for Karen the moment was charged with tension. She wondered if it was the dislike each felt for the other that was creeping into the atmosphere.

At last he spoke, saying casually, 'It was becoming rather warm in there. You obviously thought so, too.'

'Yes, I did find it a little overpowering.' Like you, she added, but silently. He was towering over her, regarding her in a way that gave her a feeling of having been stripped and, colouring, she took a swift step away from him.

'Your friend Miss Dempster has talent,' he remarked conversationally after a while. 'I've advised her to consider acting as a career.'

'Yes, she told me. Meryl's very keen on acting; it was she who persuaded me to join the company.' She was still using her stage voice, and he looked at her oddly, as if debating whether or not this was also her natural voice. However, he wasn't interested enough to inquire about it and another silence fell between them. Karen said, driven by some impulse she could neither understand nor control, because the last thing she desired was to open a conversation with him, 'Jake was saying that you're writing your next play on a boat.'

'That's correct.'

'It's to be moored at Barbados. That's a beautiful island.' She was about to mention Jean but refrained, deciding he would not be in the least interested in the fact that her sister worked on the island.

'It is beautiful, yes.'

'But you don't live there.'

'No, I prefer Grenada, mainly because it's not so touristy. It doesn't have as much to offer the visitor as Barbados.'

'It must be nice to live on a boat.' Karen's eyes were suddenly dreamy as she added, 'You'll have just the right atmosphere there. Jake says you want to be alone.'

'I do.' He sounded bored, she thought, and was not surprised when he excused himself and left her.

She walked from the patio onto the grounds, finding a dark path among the shrubs and proceeding slowly along it. Then she stopped on hearing voices from the other side of the hedge. Clint Fraser was with Sally Haworth, one of the older members of the company. Sally had obviously asked a question because Clint was saying, 'Yes, his acting was excellent for an amateur.'

'Meryl, the heroine, she's always very good too.'

'Excellent.'

'And the bitch. She—'

'Lacks finesse,' interrupted the playwright disparagingly. 'That girl couldn't act if she put everything she had into it.'

Karen gasped, the hot colour rising in her cheeks as anger and humiliation fought for supremacy. For him to have said a thing like that to one of her fellow actors! But he had been equally outspoken in that television interview, she recalled, obviously he was a man who always spoke his mind.

If only she could show him whether she could act or not! But the way she felt at the moment it would give her far more satisfaction to do him a physical injury. . . .

Chapter Two

Karen was back in her own office after having been called into the Managing Director's room to be told that, from the beginning of the following month, she would be working as private secretary to John Lacey.

'I hope you'll be as happy with him as you have been with Mr. French,' he smiled.

Out of politeness Karen was obliged to say, 'I think I will be, Mr. Smythe,' but her heart was heavy as she left the room.

At lunch time she bought a newspaper, deciding she would look for another post. And as she scanned the "Situations Vacant" column one advertisement, a square window-frame advertisement, stood out, the words dancing before her eyes. When she focused she read, "Wanted for a period of approximately six months, woman of forty-five or over for light duties on a luxury, ocean-going cabin cruiser. Duties include some cooking, cleaning, etc. Telephone for interview." The number followed. Karen read the advertisement again, then scanned the rest of the column, but her eyes returned over and over again to the advertisement put in by Clint Fraser, and inevitably she was hearing his derisive criticism of her acting.

She found herself studying the advertisement with concentrated attention as an idea was conceived. Why not apply for the post? After all, she had nothing to lose. And if she should happen to be fortunate enough to obtain the job, what a satisfying revenge she would have when, in six months time, she could confound him by revealing her true identity. He would be forced to eat those words about her inability to act!

The interview was to take place in a small private room at the Savoy Hotel in London where the playwright was staying while in England, and Karen had known a tense and breathless moment when, having rung the number and heard Clint Fraser's voice, she had given him her name—though omitting her Christian name—saying she was applying for the post.

'Miss Waring,' he had repeated, then given his own name and Karen had breathed freely again. Just as she had suspected, Clint Fraser had not bothered to memorise her name when given it by Jake when he had introduced them at the party.

The interview was for eleven o'clock the following Saturday morning and Karen rose early so as to give herself ample time to effect the transformation in her appearance. And when at last she was ready she felt just about as confident as it was possible to be. For the face and figure which she saw in the long, gilt-framed mirror faultlessly portrayed those of a woman in her mid-forties. She had dry, graying hair taken severely back from her furrowed brow; her face was pale, the lips almost colourless. The eyes alone had caused Karen some concern, but she had soon solved this problem by the use of horn-rimmed spectacles with clear glass in them. The dress, of a dull gray linen-type material, hung loosely, hiding the seductive curves beneath its austere folds and the shapely legs within its length. Only at the neck was it tight, fastened up high, to give an added severity to the face above it.

'Hmm. . . .' approved Karen with a satisfied smile as she picked up a heavy velour coat she borrowed from an elderly neighbor in the flat next door. 'Yes, you've done a most excellent job, Miss Karen Waring! I congratulate you!'

She was congratulating herself again an hour later when, having entered the room at the Savoy Hotel, she saw no sign of recognition on the face of the man standing there with his back to the window.

'Miss Waring.' The pewter-gray eyes ran over her figure indifferently before returning to her face, to settle there. He seemed to frown, as if he deplored women who used cosmetics too freely. However, as his interest was in her suitability as a servant rather than in her looks, he began briskly to ask the relevant questions. These were answered, but sometimes the answers were gone into a little more deeply as, for instance, when he asked why she should want to leave a perfectly good post as private secretary to take on something that was to last only six months.

'I want a complete change,' she replied frankly. 'I

know I can get another, similar post at the end of the six months.'

'You're sure?' His firm, finely modulated voice held a trace of anxiety. 'You're no longer young, remember, and so you might have difficulty. Secretarial posts are not so plentiful as they were a few years ago.'

'I'm willing to take the risk,' she said, looking away to hide her expression. 'I've always wanted to travel, and when you said on the telephone that your boat was to be moored at Barbados, that was an added incentive because, you see, my young sister lives there, and if I did get the post we'd be able to see one another regularly, which would be nice for us both, as we haven't any other relatives at all.' Karen held her breath, aware that for one vital moment she had forgotten to use her "mature" voice. But there was no sign that Clint Fraser had noticed, and in fact, he was looking rather bored, as if he were wishing the interview were at an end.

'You've had no experience in the kind of work I should expect you to do.' It was a statement but he looked at her, expecting a comment.

'Only that I look after myself in my flat,' returned Karen. 'And I think I'm a fairly good cook,' she added, watching his face intently, trying to find some clue as to whether or not he was favourably impressed. But she read nothing; his dark face was inscrutable, like a mask.

However, his next words were heartening, to say the least.

'I'm interested in the fact that you have a sister on the island whom you could see regularly. When I'm working on a play I work solidly for the whole day and, therefore, I should not want to see or hear you from the time you serve my breakfast at eight o'clock in the morning, until you bring in my dinner at nine in the evening.' He paused, giving her an opportunity to speak but she said nothing, merely waiting for him to continue. 'I have a small suite at one end of the boat, and this consists of a study, a small sitting room, a bathroom and a very small galley where I can make myself coffee when I want it. You would prepare me a snack lunch and leave it there. You would clean up the suite while I'm at breakfast, and be out of it by the time I'd finished.' Another pause, and this time Karen did speak, to ask what other accommodations the cruiser had.

'There is a dining room, I suppose, and a galley,' she said, 'but what about the cabins? I'd scarcely be able to clean the rest of the boat without making a sound.'

'My suite's right at one end and the galley's at the other. Your work would mainly be in there—the preparation of the food and the washing—' He stopped, frowning at her as if he considered the discussions of such things to be beneath him. 'As for the other cleaning—' he shrugged offhandedly, '—well, you'd have to do it either very early in the morning or late at night.'

'Yes. . . .' She nodded automatically.

'You'll have gathered,' he went on briskly, 'that you will have most of the day free. I'd prefer that you leave the boat as soon as possible and not return until it's time for you to prepare my evening meal. I like to know I'm entirely alone when I'm working. At home I have servants around and also gardeners. There are altogether too many distractions and it's because I'm trying to get away from these distractions that I've decided to use my boat.' He went on to say that the boat would be moored at the private jetty of the Smuggler's Cove Hotel, which was owned by a friend of his. The jetty was situated at an isolated part of the beach not accessible to the hotel guests, and so he could be sure of both privacy and quietness—the notice "No Guests Beyond This Point" usually being effective.

When Clint Fraser said that she would be expected to leave the boat for more than eight hours each day, Karen had wondered what on earth she would do with herself all that time. But on hearing him mention the Smuggler's Cove Hotel she could scarcely believe her ears, for it was right next to the Vervain Hotel in which her sister worked, and as Jean had a small bungalow on the hotel grounds, one of several provided for the more privileged on the staff, Karen could go there, using it as a second home, as it were. Yes, that would be fine, because, once she arrived at the bungalow she could get rid of her disguise for the next eight hours or so. She could don a bikini and sunbathe. It would be like a prolonged holiday! She had not thought of taking any clothes other than would be suitable to her "mature" age, just in case, by some mischance, Clint Fraser should see them. But now she could take what she liked, and leave them at her sister's.

'I've one or two more people to interview,' Clint was saying a short while later, 'but I'll let you know, by letter, not later than Tuesday.'

'Thank you, Mr. Fraser.' Karen rose from the chair. He opened the door for her and stood to one side.

'If I decide to employ you,' he said as she made to pass him, 'I should want you a fortnight today. I shall be flying to my home in Grenada on Thursday week and you would follow two days later. My boat's at Grenada and we shall sail with a crew from there to Barbados where the boat will be moored for about six months. The crew will then leave; they've already been hired by a South American family who are cruising the Caribbean for several months.'

The letter came three days later.

She had gotten the job!

There was her notice to give in and, fortunately for her, her boss put in a good word for her and she was able to leave without giving the customary one month notice. There was the rushing around, the handing over of her flat to an estate agent who would let it for her. There were clothes to buy, friends to see, and a final dinner at a small hotel to which Karen invited Meryl and two other friends. During the meal they all wanted to know everything, and Helen, Karen's friend from school days, was especially enthusiastic, simply because the masquerade appealed to her sense of adventure. Glenda, the other friend, foretold all sorts of snags and risks, and finally, the sack.

'He'll see through the disguise eventually,' she sighed. 'Karen, you must be crazy to have given up your excellent job for this. I wouldn't be in your shoes when he finds out!'

'What can he do?' shrugged Karen. 'As you say, he

can send me packing, and probably raise the roof at being deceived, but he can't do me any physical injury.'

'Well. . . .'

'You carry on,' enthused Helen. 'I'll book a holiday in Barbados and come and see you.'

'Have you thought what it's going to be like with that stuff on your face all day?' asked Glenda dismally.

'It won't be on all day.' Karen went on to explain what she had been told by Clint Fraser at the interview.

'You'll have the whole day to yourself!' exclaimed Meryl enviously. 'Good lord, that's not a job, it's a picnic!'

'So you'll be able to wash your makeup off until it's time to return to the boat?' interposed Helen. 'You'll be able to do it at your sister's, of course?'

'Yes. It'll be a relief, I must admit, because it isn't at all comfortable, wearing it too long.'

'Nor will it be comfortable wearing drab clothes,' added Glenda with a doleful shake of her head.

'It's to be hoped,' said Meryl thoughtfully, 'that Mr. Fraser doesn't ever want you in the night—'

'In the night? Why should he?'

'If he took ill, or anything. You'd not have time for making yourself up, and so the cat would really be out of the bag.'

'It's not an impossibility that he'd need me in the night,' Karen admitted, but added that she was not going to let a thing like that worry her. 'He seems so strong that I can't imagine him sick!' said she, reflecting on his healthy bronzed colouring and superb physique.

'You're going to get yourself into such a tangle,' warned Glenda woefully.

'Your sister'll be staggered when she knows what you've done,' laughed Meryl. 'Oh, but I do think you're adventurous, Karen!'

'Not adventurous but foolhardy,' from Glenda with a sigh.

'Oh, shut up, Glenda, you old pessimist,' chided Helen. 'I only wish I could have done something like this. Not only is Karen going to travel, but she's going to have fun as well, hoodwinking that horrid Clint Fraser.'

The following day Karen flew to Grenada, being met at the airport by Clint Fraser himself who took her by car to his home, a lovely modern villa set in extensive grounds overlooking the Caribbean Sea. Everything about the villa and gardens spelled luxury and good taste. The house had high airy rooms beautifully furnished, the grounds were immaculately kept with smooth velvet lawns, flowerbeds and borders, two fountains cascading into ornamental pools; statuary and terraces and sunken rose gardens, and towering over it all, graceful palms of many varieties, and royal poincianas and frangipani trees. Karen was enchanted with it and on one occasion had almost forgotten her role and would have exclaimed in her natural voice but she pulled herself up just in time. After that she was very guarded, assuming the kind of reserve that would be expected of a mature woman of forty-five years of age. She stayed the night at his home and the following day they sailed to Barbados where the crew was dismissed.

The *Fair Mermaid* had been moored at Barbados for over a week, and Karen had fallen into a pleasant routine where, donning an apron, she would prepare her employer's breakfast and take it in to him precisely at eight o'clock every morning. While he was eating it she would rush around with duster and vacuum cleaner, tidying up Clint's suite, but taking care to replace, exactly as she found it, anything on his desk. After breakfast she would clear away the dishes, wash them up, tidy the dining room for the evening, and then she would go off the boat and make for Jean's bungalow, where, after taking off her makeup, she would bathe and change—having already taken her clothes there—and if Jean was not too busy at reception, they would have a chat over morning coffee and Karen would then take a book on to the hotel's private beach. Jean came off duty at six in the evening, so the sisters had about an hour together before Karen began to change her personality in preparation for returning to the boat.

'It's wonderful, seeing so much of you!' Jean had said more than once during the past week. 'It was the greatest piece of luck that you landed a job like that!'

'I know it. I've scarcely anything to do. I have Mr. Fraser's washing and ironing, and my own, of course, but I manage to do that before I serve his breakfast, as I'm up at half-past six. It leaves me all this time to myself.' Already she had acquired a lovely honey-peach tan, and the front of her hair was becoming attractively lighter where the sun had begun to bleach it.

'You get prettier all the time,' Jean told her, watching as she began to unscrew several bottles in preparation for putting on her new face. 'Aren't you afraid of damaging your skin?' she asked, a frown creasing her brow.

'I admit I don't like having all this on my face for too long, but it's a case of having to when I'm on the boat—except at night, of course.'

'The risk seems so great,' mused Jean. 'He could find you out, you know.'

'I'm not going to let myself worry about it,' returned Karen carelessly.

'You've more courage than I!'

'Rubbish! Look at the way you threw up your job to take this one you have here—just because it was in the Caribbean.'

'And you threw up yours for a similar reason. But at least I can be myself all the time. How you manage not to give yourself away I don't know. Are you sure you never inadvertently use your natural voice?'

'I scarcely ever speak to the man,' returned Karen ruefully. 'He says good morning and I reply, and then he might say he'd like something done that's extra to my normal jobs and I'll answer. The other day he sent me shopping and I naturally spoke to him a little then, and at night when I serve him his dinner we might exchange civilities, but that's the limit of my need to converse so it isn't difficult to remember to use my assumed voice.'

This routine continued for another month and then two changes took place almost at once. First, Karen received a letter from Helen to say that she was coming over for a holiday, flying from London in less than a week's time.

'I know it's not giving you much notice, Karen,' Helen went on, 'but as it's not the busy season over there I'm sure you can get me accommodations. I made up my mind suddenly because one of my colleagues at work asked me to change holidays with her, as her mother was to go into the hospital in August and she wants to be off work at that time, so I obliged, taking my holidays now. I'm coming over for three weeks.'

Karen went at once and rented an apartment on the grounds of the Coral Court Hotel, paying the money for the three weeks. But the day after the arrival of Helen's letter Jean was told she was being temporarily transferred to one of the company's hotels on the island of St Lucia.

'Helen can have my bungalow,' Jean offered.

'She'll be delighted,' returned Karen, fully aware that she could not get the money back for the apartment but surmising that Helen would be more comfortable in Jean's bungalow. 'But are you sure you don't mind?'

'Quite sure; I know Helen well enough. Besides, I'd feel better if someone were in the bungalow at night.'

As Karen had prophesied, Helen was thrilled at the idea of having Jean's bungalow for the three weeks of her stay, although naturally she paid Karen for the apartment. Karen hired a taxi and met her at the airport, saying she was taking her straight back to the bungalow, from which Jean had departed two days previously.

'I go to the bungalow each day,' Karen said. 'It'll be in the evenings that you might feel lonely, but if you dine at the hotel that'll take care of a couple of hours.'

'Don't worry about me, Karen. You know me well enough to be sure I'll find plenty to do.'

'I'm usually at the bungalow by about ten to eleven o'clock.'

'And we've all day together?'

'Yes, until about seven, then I have to leave in order to be back to prepare Mr. Fraser's dinner.' They were entering the long, tree-lined drive to the hotel and Helen began to enthuse about the flowers and the smells and the white sandy shore seen through the exotic vegetation of the grounds. The bungalows were away from the hotel, delightfully set in a secluded spot with private access to the beach.

After Helen had settled in—Karen showed her to the bedroom and helped her unpack her two suitcases—the girls went out through a tapestry of exotic color, across two wide lawns, to the terrace of the hotel where they had a buffet lunch washed down with a fruity white wine. Helen kept asking questions about Karen's job, about her sister's job, and about the island generally. Karen answered, and a pleasant hour was spent over the buffet.

'You lucky blighter,' sighed Helen leaning back in her chair and staring out to where a graceful white-sailed luxury yacht rode its languid path over the waves. 'You'll never want to come back to England.'

'I might try for another post here when this one folds up.'

'Jean might be able to help.'

Karen nodded.

'I've thought about an hotel,' she admitted. 'I've met Jean's boss, the manager here, and I'm sure he'd be interested in offering me something.'

'Mr. Fraser could just want to keep you on, when he writes his next play.'

'I wouldn't stay, Helen. It's a super post, I admit, but the life I live isn't natural.'

'The dual personality, you mean?'

'Yes. I couldn't keep it up indefinitely.'

'But it's worth it for the six months?'

'Of course.'

'How is the play progressing?'

'I've no idea. Mr. Fraser's the most uncommunicative man I've ever met. He'd never mention his work to a mere underling.'

'I'd like to see his face when he sees yours!' said Helen, laughing heartily. 'When it's all over and you unmask and let him know he's been duped.'

'I'm looking forward to that!'

At half-past six Karen began to put on her makeup and at seven o'clock she was ready to leave the bungalow. Helen could only stare in admiration at the change in Karen's appearance.

'You'd have deceived even me!' she exclaimed and meant it.

When Karen met her friend the following morning she said delightedly, 'Mr. Fraser says I can have the whole day off. He's dining out this evening so you and

I can go somewhere for dinner.' It would be a little trying tonight, thought Karen, having to come to the bungalow, perhaps very late, put on her disguise, and then go to the boat. However, it would be worth it, and it had nothing to do with her employer what time she came in so long as she did not disturb him.

'There's a dinner dance at a place called Sam Lord's Castle tonight,' said Helen. 'It's advertised in the lobby of the Vervain Hotel.'

'Shall we go?' Karen was excited. This would be the first time she had been out at night since leaving England. 'I'd love to wear a long dress and really look myself!'

'Fine. I wanted to go but wouldn't have gone on my own.'

'It should be fun. What time does it start?'

'Dinner's at nine. Will we have to book?' Karen nodded her head and Helen went on, 'I'll phone from the hotel then,' and she went off to do it. A few hours later Karen was saying, 'I wish I'd brought all my clothes with me.' She and Helen were in their bikinis after having lunched at the hotel. 'My evening dresses are still in my cabin, and I've been meaning to bring them here but never really expected to have evenings off. It was only an afterthought that I brought a couple of long dresses. It would have saved me putting on the disguise again.' She was frowning, wondering how she could have come to overlook the fact that there was no need for her to return to the boat, seeing that her employer did not require dinner.

'What time will he be leaving? You could perhaps avoid the necessity of the disguise if you timed your return correctly.'

It was risky but Karen decided to take a chance.

'I'll leave it as late as I can,' she said, aware that the quickly falling darkness would be an aid to her slipping on to the boat unseen. And she happened to be lucky, because when she was a fair distance away she saw him come out on deck and she dodged behind a tree, watching as he came swiftly down the gangway, a tall, impressive figure immaculately clad in pearl-gray slacks and draped-line jacket, his shirt gleaming white against his burnt sienna throat. Karen caught her breath . . . what a superlatively handsome man he was!

Sam Lord's Castle was an hotel today, but it had a dark and bloodthirsty past, the legend of Sam Lord being that he caused ships to be wrecked by hanging lanterns in the trees. These swayed about in the wind and appeared to be the lights of Carlisle Harbour which misled the ships' crews and so caused the wrecks. The cargoes were raided and taken ashore to add their value to the coffers of the infamous Samuel Lord, the man who was reputed to have imprisoned his wife in the castle dungeon, from which she managed to escape to England by bribing her slave jailer with jewels. But this evening there was no sign of its grim past. On the contrary, the atmosphere was one of gaiety, where the women in their evening dresses and the men in casual but elegant suits, gathered to socialize in the lounge, glasses in their hands.

The restaurant, subtly lit by candles and lamps hidden in the thick green foliage of plants growing in huge pots, was large, with tables placed round a centre dancing space. Karen and Helen had a table well away from this dance space, and next to them was another table occupied by two young men who were obviously on holiday on the island. One smiled at Karen and then Helen, and within minutes the four were chatting as they began the first course. By the time the second course arrived the two tables had been joined to make a table for four. Names were exchanged, and Bill got up to dance with Karen while his friend, Derek, danced with Helen. And it was when they were just about to come from the floor that Karen gave a little gasp and stared at the tall, distinguished figure of her employer. He was guiding his partner to a table where six other people were sitting, his hand beneath the girl's elbow, and on his face a smile which was a revelation to Karen. What a difference in his appearance! He was actually laughing now, she noticed, and his dark pewter-gray eyes were laughing, too, as they looked into his partner's upturned face.

'Anything wrong?' asked Bill, a trifle concerned. 'You look as if you've seen a ghost.'

A ghost. . . . No, a man very much alive, a vital personality, a man obviously admired by his companions because every one of them looked up to smile when he reached the table. He was, decided Karen, the most distinguished man in the room.

'No, it's nothing,' she said to Bill, but a moment later she was saying softly to her friend, 'That's my boss—the famous Clint Fraser. It never dawned on me that this is where he'd be dining.'

Helen followed the direction of her eyes and gave a laugh.

'Wouldn't it be a lark if he asked you to dance with him?'

Karen's eyes twinkled. It would certainly add a little spice, she agreed.

Watching him in the company of others, Karen was so fascinated by the change that she could not take her eyes off him for very long at a time, so it was inevitable that he should in the end become conscious of her concentrated stare. His eyes met hers; she coloured and lowered her lashes.

She determinedly kept her eyes away for the duration of the meal, which was a pleasant, leisurely one and it was only to be expected that, while they chatted, the men should ask questions about the two girls. Helen had no difficulties; she told them she was on holiday and staying at the house of a friend. Karen, already having anticipated the question, also had an answer ready.

'No, I'm not on holiday, I work part-time and have been spending the rest of my time with my sister, who lives here. My job's one I can't talk about,' she added and there was the sort of firmness in her voice that instantly precluded any further questions from the men.

They were staying at the Coral Gables and had hired a car for the fortnight. They had already had one week, and they suggested the girls go about with them for the second week. This Karen had no intention of doing, and neither had Helen. So when the invitation came it was politely rejected, the men taking it in good part, with Bill saying good humoredly, 'Fair enough, Karen. But you won't cut us if we happen to meet again?'

'Of course not,' she assured him. She offered no explanations for being reticent about her work, but she felt that as her life—which could have been complicated—was running smoothly, she ought not to run any risks. It was improbable, but by no means impossible, that her employer would require more from her than he was getting at present. If, for instance, he decided to take a break from his writing it might be that he would entertain, and it would fall to her to do all the work involved. She had never expected this present state of affairs to continue unbroken for six months.

When the meal was over some of the guests went outside, while others congregated in the lounge, to spend the rest of the evening drinking and socializing. Karen and Helen went to a handsomely decorated room which Sam Lord had embellished with late Georgian woodwork and delicate plaster work on the ceiling, done by an artist who had worked on Windsor Castle. Here at one end was a raised dais on which a steel band was playing. On the polished floor several couples danced. It was an "excuse me" and Helen said, 'I dare you to dance with him, Karen.'

Karen turned, her eyes gleaming with mischief as they wandered from her friend's challenging stare to the couple dancing close together on the edge of the floor.

'I accept your dare,' she returned with a toss of her head and went forward resolutely to tap her employer on the shoulder. She received a scowling glance from the girl and a frowning one from her partner.

'Excuse me,' she said politely in her normal low-toned voice and Clint had no alternative but to leave his glamorous partner and allow Karen to slip into his arms.

She was recalling what he had said about not intending to pander to the whim of some female avid for romance and, an imp of mischief suddenly entering into her, she decided to flirt with him, just as a matter of interest, to see how he would react. She leaned away, fluttering her lashes as she said, her voice at its sweetest, 'Are you on holiday here?'

'No,' briefly and curtly, 'I am not.'

That was enough to put any girl off, thought Karen chuckling to herself.

'Working, then?' No answer and she added, quite undaunted by his manner, 'It's a lovely island, isn't it? So romantic. . . .' Her voice trailed away to a seductive silence; she was acting a part she had once played, the part of a scheming woman determined to get her man. 'Yes, so romantic. Don't you agree?'

He held her from him, his grip on her arms tightening ruthlessly.

'All islands in the Caribbean are romantic.'

'They are? You've been to them all?'

He pulled her to him again, forced to the action in order to avoid collision with another couple.

'Not all,' he replied curtly.

He was angry, she thought, amusement rippling through her. That imp of mischief impelled her to say, 'It's rather hot in here, don't you think? Shall we go outside into the cool for a little while?' That would disconcert her phlegmatic employer, she thought, peeping up at him through her lashes. His mouth was set, his jaw flexed. She had the greatest difficulty in suppressing laughter, but she did manage it and her voice was husky and coaxing as she added, curling her fingers against his shoulders and then deliberately allowing them to touch his nape in a sexy little caress. 'There's a full moon, and stars. And the air's scented by flowers. Let's go out,' she urged. 'Just for five minutes?'

He looked down contemptuously.

'Five minutes?' with a fractional lift of his brows. 'You don't give yourself much time, do you?'

'A kiss doesn't take very long.'

'It just depends on who's doing the kissing,' he returned unexpectedly and a certain quality in his voice set her pulses tingling. But before she had time to respond the music stopped and without so much as a word he left her to make her own way back to the table. Bill and Derek were still standing on the edge of the dance space, chatting to the two girls with whom they had been dancing.

'What happened?' Helen wanted to know. 'You look ready to burst with laughter.'

'I tried to flirt with him.'

'That shouldn't have caused you any difficulty, not with your experience as the bitchy one.'

'I asked him to go out to the garden with me.'

At that Helen's eyes widened to their fullest extent.

'That was rather risky, wasn't it? I mean, it's all very well in a play but—' She broke off, shaking her head as her eyes sought the object of their discussion across the room. 'I'd not like to trust that one in the dark!'

'Oh, I knew he'd not take me up on it,' returned Karen airily. 'Don't forget, I know him well, being his housekeeper. That man might write plays but he hasn't an ounce of romance in him. I told you why he didn't want a young woman for his housekeeper, didn't I?'

'You did, but what about this girl he's with now?' Helen was thoughtful as she continued to stare at the handsome profile of Karen's employer. 'I'm no real judge of the opposite sex but I've had my moments, and I'd never believe he's cold—at least, not when he gets going.'

'Gets going?' laughed Karen. 'What on earth do you mean by that?'

'I'll bet he can be as ardent as the rest.'

Karen fell silent, reflecting on how he was on the boat, totally absorbed in his work. She would have said he was as cold as stone but, watching him with that girl, she was beginning to wonder if she had made a mistake.

Chapter Three

As the evening progressed Karen became restless for some reason which she could not understand. All she knew was that her eyes would repeatedly wander toward Clint Fraser and his party, and especially to the glamourous girl who seemed to be coming in for more than her share of his attention. He sometimes caught Karen's eye and she noticed that he would frown. Obviously he believed she was attracted by him and the knowledge vexed her so much that, in the end, she politely excused herself and left the other three to wander out onto the moonlit grounds where the air was balmy and the grassy lawns cushion-soft beneath her feet. She walked on, among some of the loveliest trees and shrubs and exotic flowers she had ever seen. There were flamboyants and casuarinas, the beautiful pride of India, the frangipani and the pink poui and the delightful African tulip tree. It was too much! Her whole being was affected by the sheer beauty around her. One or two people were strolling, like herself, and stopping now and then to admire particularly beautiful flowers, highlighted by the lanterns in the trees above their heads. Karen, her senses a little drugged by it all, could quite easily create pictures of Sam Lord's lamps in the coconut trees on the coast of Long Bay, swaying in the strong tropical breeze, guiding ships to what should have been a haven but was in reality the treacherous reef, where they floundered, a prey to Sam Lord's slaves who would then set out and capture the cargoes for their master.

Karen had to smile at her mind wanderings. The stories of Sam Lord's wickedness were legendary, anyway, so it was quite possible that they were, in the main, untrue.

She found herself leaving the more sophisticated part of the grounds and entering a rougher, wilder region where the Atlantic rollers, sweeping into the shore, had ruthlessly killed the vegetation, leaving only the gaunt and twisted skeletons of what had once been a forest of beautiful trees. She stopped, her slender figure outlined against the arc of the sky where it touched the horizon, when suddenly she heard the snapping of a dead branch beneath someone's foot and she swung around, nerves alert. Clint Fraser! He saw her and halted, then turned abruptly to retrace his steps, swiftly and determinedly as if he were obeying an angry urge to put distance between him and Karen in as little time as possible.

She shrugged and smiled to herself, yet at the same time she was aware of confused thoughts through which emerged a vague sense of disappointment. What was wrong with her tonight? She had felt on top of the world a few hours ago at the idea of coming to this function, dressing up for the occasion in a long flowing evening gown of midnight blue cotton, gossamer fine, like silk. Low cut at the neck, it was rather more revealing than any other dress she owned, but she loved the way the bodice fitted snugly to her curves and waist, and the way the intricate folds swayed when she walked and danced. Yes, she had been very happy a few hours ago, but now. . . .

Shrugging off the tinge of dejection which she could not understand anyway, and, with the intention of returning to the hotel, but not by the route chosen by her employer, she turned inland, only to discover that she was making things difficult for herself, as the ground was littered with the aerial roots of the giant banyan trees that predominated in the whole of the area. After catching her foot in one of these she decided it would be wiser to go back and proceed along the shore. But no sooner had she turned then she caught her foot again and automatically extended her hands to break her fall. The next instant she had come with a thud against a hard male body and before she could even utter her cry of protest it was effectively smothered by the bruising contact of the man's mouth on hers. She began to struggle and was told roughly to stop. Clint Fraser! He must have been strolling along a narrow path which just happened to come out at the very point where she had tripped. His name almost burst from her lips in her fury and astonishment. What a difference! The passion of his kiss brought starkly to mind what Helen had said about him.

'Let go of me!' she cried, managing to lean away from him. 'What do you think you're doing!'

'Giving you what you've asked for—' His mouth came down again, the kiss dominating and sensuous as it forced her lips apart. For long, heady moments she was compelled to endure his total domination as he held her, pressed to his iron-hard body, her arms pinned against her sides. Gasping for breath when at last he held her from him, she could scarcely speak for the white-hot fury that possessed her.

'You beast!' she hissed. 'I never asked for this!'

'Come off it,' he sneered. 'In there you offered me an invitation, and now, when I'd avoided you over there on the shore, you deliberately followed me—'

'I did *not* follow you,' she flared. 'It was just coincidence that we met here! I'd tripped over some roots!'

'What sort of a fool do you think you're trying to convince? And what's the idea anyway? You're so damned transparent—it's plain what you want—'

'Oh!' she quivered, 'you shan't say that about me, I—' The rest was lost in the blind fury of her resistance as, laughing at her protest, he crushed her body to his in a punishing embrace. She struggled desperately at the significant movement of his hand as it slid up from her waist, and at last, driven by wild uncontrollable fury, she kicked out viciously at his shins and to her satisfaction and relief his hold slackened and she was able to free herself. But she leaned, panting, against the wide trunk of the banyan tree whose roots had been the cause of all the trouble, and to her chagrin she felt the hot tears falling down her cheeks.

'You damned vixen,' he began but it was her turn to interrupt.

'And you damned brute!' she inserted before he could continue. 'If you're prone to these caveman tactics then why the devil don't you go and find someone who'll enjoy them? You ought to be among animals, not humans!' Her temper was like a searing hot furnace, but she was still weak from his treatment of her. 'I wish I were a man,' she fumed, 'I'd strangle you with my bare hands!'

'If you'd been a man,' he returned mildly, 'this situation would never have came about.'

'I'm in no mood for satire,' she flung at him. 'Keep your witticisms for those who can appreciate them!'

He said nothing, but just stood there, in the moonlight, looking at her. She wondered if he could see her tears and with a furious gesture she knuckled her eyes.

'What are you standing there for?' she demanded when at last she had all her breath back. 'Clear off! I should think you know by now that you've made a blunder!'

'I agree,' he murmured in a very soft voice. 'But, my girl, you'd have been the one to make the blunder if it had been any other man you'd been playing around with. You're damned lucky it was me. Just what was the idea?' His voice had risen slightly, and there was an imperious demand within its depths. 'Well, I'm waiting?'

She swallowed, unable to find anything to say because it was understandable that he would ask a question like that after the subtle invitation she had given him when they were dancing. And this unexpected meeting. . . . She could accept that he believed it to have been engineered by her. The implication of it all brought colour flooding to her cheeks as she realised that what had begun as mere mischief, born of pique that he had criticised her acting, had resulted in his condemning her a no-good, a girl who would deliberately throw herself at any man. Her only consolation was that he did not know who she was. 'I'm still waiting,' came the stern request again but all she did was turn away with the intention of leaving him, but she was wrong. Without warning she was seized and thoroughly shaken, then pushed against the tree again, for support.

'Watch yourself in the future!' he warned darkly. 'You might not escape so easily!' and on that he swung away, his tall figure soon melting into the darkness until all she saw was a vague form that eventually became no more than a shadow.

Karen, in her disguise, stood in the galley, over the stove, cooking eggs and bacon, her thoughts on last night and her encounter with the man to whom she was about to serve breakfast. And suddenly it was all a big joke, with only the humorous side affecting her, and she laughed softly to herself. Helen, she recalled, had seen the funny side right away, and had only refrained from laughter because Karen was so distressed, and still furious too, mainly because she was carrying bruises where Clint's fingers had eaten mercilessly into her flesh when he had shaken her.

With breakfast on the silver tray she went to the dining saloon and knocked.

'Come in.'

'Good morning, Mr. Fraser,' she said in her "mature" voice as she placed the tray on the sideboard. 'Did you have a pleasant evening?'

'So-so,' he replied noncommittally, and sat down, ready to be waited upon.

Karen put a glass of fruit juice in front of him, then the heated plate on which was a small amount of bacon and an egg.

'You don't eat enough,' she murmured. 'It's not enough for a man.'

'I appreciate your motherly concern, Miss Waring, but what I eat is my own affair. I assure you that if I wanted more I should not hesitate to ask for it.'

Karen had already turned away, her lips quivering at his reference to her "motherly concern".

'Do you want sandwiches today for lunch or a meat salad?' she asked as she placed the toast rack down on the table.

'I shall probably be going out to lunch, but I'm not sure.'

'Oh. . . . And dinner?'

'Again, I can't say.' He paused and a frown knit his brow. 'I'll let you know about both meals before you go off. What time will you be leaving the boat?'

'In about two hours,' she answered, trying to think if there were any other chores besides a small amount of washing and the tidying up of the galley afterward.

'Very well. I shall know in less than two hours whether or not I'll be having my meals here.'

She looked at him a moment, then ventured to ask if there were any special reason for his not knowing if he wanted his snack lunch prepared and his dinner later.

'My work's not progressing as it should. My heroine's unsatisfactory,' he admitted and Karen stared in amazement that he would unbend sufficiently to confide in her.

'Unsatisfactory, Mr. Fraser,' she echoed, encouraged by his manner. 'In what way?'

'I want her to be unusual, unpredictable and intriguing.' He paused in thought, frowning. 'No,' he murmured almost to himself, 'she isn't at all what I want.' He looked at Karen. 'It sometimes happens and there's only one remedy. I take time off for recreation. If my writing goes well in the next hour or so it'll go well all day, but if not—then, I shall be having my meals at an hotel.' His eyes flickered over her indifferently, taking in the drab dress beneath the white apron, the graying hair, the pale insipid lips. Something stirred within Karen—no more than the fluttering of a pulse, perhaps, so intangible as not to be disturbing.

He picked up the glass of fruit juice and, taking the action as a silent dismissal, she turned and left the saloon.

Within a couple of hours she had done all her chores and was on her way to the Vervain Hotel and the pretty little bungalow on the grounds. She had a key and let herself in, as Helen would already have left for the beach.

Twenty minutes later her disguise was gone.

'This is little less than one long holiday for you,' commented Helen enviously when, having joined her on the beach, Karen discarded her wrap and settled down to soak up the sun and increase her tan.

'I admit it. And what do you think? I've the whole day off. Mr. Fraser doesn't want either lunch or dinner. He said early this morning that as the play's not going as he wants it to, he might leave it and give himself a little recreation. It's his heroine; she isn't doing what he wants her to. She—' Karen stopped. 'Is something wrong, Helen?'

'You're off this evening?'

'Yes, that's right.'

'I've made a date with Bill. I didn't think you'd be off—'

'It's all right,' Karen interrupted swiftly. 'I'll find something to do.'

Helen frowned, absently picking up a bottle of suntan lotion and unscrewing the top.

'I don't care for your being on your own,' she began, when Karen interrupted her again to assure her that she would be quite all right.

'I shall do some extra chores on the boat,' she added. 'Then I'll be able to have my days off with you without feeling I've neglected anything. The windows need cleaning for one thing.'

'You're sure?' Helen was still doubtful. 'I wish I'd known.'

'I'm quite sure,' returned Karen and changed the subject, asking her friend if she liked her new bikini.

'Yes, very much—at least, what there is of it,' laughed Helen. 'I wonder what the great Mr. Clint

Fraser would say if he saw his middle-aged housekeeper now?'

'I don't know. . . .' Karen stretched out her long slender legs. 'I really don't know. . . .'

After spending the rest of the morning sunbathing, with the occasional swim in between, the girls donned their beach wraps and went into the hotel for a buffet lunch. And no sooner were they being shown to a table than Karen's eyes met those of her employer. She coloured hotly under his narrowed stare, and turned away, wishing she could escape, go somewhere else for her lunch but already Helen was on her way to the buffet table and Karen had no alternative than to follow.

Clint was joined by the girl he was with last night and they began to chat as they proceeded along the heavily laden table. Karen could not take her eyes off Clint, whose height seemed to dominate the whole room. He was smiling and his face was transformed.

He was charm itself.

Suddenly aware of Karen's concentrated interest he flashed her an unfathomable glance, and a satirical smile touched his lips seconds later, when her colour rose again.

'What's up?' asked Helen when they were seated on the terrace, with the yellow birds flitting around, cheekily waiting to swoop and steal a beakful of sugar from the basin on the table. 'You look all hot and bothered.'

'It's Clint Fraser,' snapped Karen, taking a breath. 'He's here! When he said he'd be having his meals at an hotel I naturally expected it would be the Smuggler's Cove because that's the nearest one to where the boat's moored. But instead, he has to come here!'

'Well, there's no reason why he shouldn't,' rejoined Helen reasonably. 'Have you been talking to him?'

'No—we just looked at one another!'

Helen burst out laughing, and at that moment Clint happened to reach their table on his way to one in the far corner to join the girl already sitting there. He glanced down, eyes glinting, and yet there was a dash of amusement in them too as he looked at Karen.

'Oh, lord!' exclaimed Karen, faintly distressed. 'I wonder what he thinks. He's sure to conclude we were making fun of him.'

'So what? Karen, pet, you are forgetting that you have *two* roles, not one. To him, you're an unknown. His colourless little housekeeper has nothing at all to do with you.'

Karen had to laugh.

'Do you know, Helen, it's becoming exceedingly difficult to separate myself—I mean, to disassociate my real self totally from the person I've assumed. Do you know what I mean?'

'Perfectly.' Helen picked up her fork and studied what was on her plate for a moment, obviously interested in the delicious variety of foods she had chosen. 'Isn't that what I've just said?' she went on belatedly, still absorbed in the delicacies before her. 'You're not remembering you're *two*. And it's essential that you do, because if you happen to give the game away then you're sacked! I can't see that man making any excuses for the kind of deceit which you are practising. It wouldn't surprise me if he lost his temper and gave you a slap.'

'He wouldn't dare!' protested Karen wrathfully. 'I'd scratch his eyes out!'

'If you got the chance.' Helen at last chose a piece of lobster and popped it into her mouth. 'Hmm. . . . I shall never get back to the beans on toast I usually have for my lunch at the office. This is scrumptious!'

Karen's eyes were on Clint Fraser's glamorous companion. She was in bright yellow shorts and a scanty sun-top. Her tan was glorious, her pale gold hair a halo for a beautiful face. Clint was talking to her, while she was fluttering her lashes, and at times making play with her hands in that sort of way which reminded Karen of a model or a ballet dancer. For sure that girl knew how to make a man notice her!

When the lunch was finished, Helen went off to the bathroom and Karen got up and walked to the wrought iron rail that ornamented the edge of the terrace. Within a few seconds she was hearing a familiar voice say,

'So we meet again.' He came to her from behind and let his eyes rove over her slender figure. Her beach coat was open to reveal the delectable curves of a seductive, suntanned body. 'You've gotten over last night, it seems?'

'Except for the bruises!' she snapped, then coloured painfully, astonished that she could make an admission which seemed to savour of the intimate.

'You deserved more than bruises, my girl! You invited me to take you outside and kiss you—which surely meant more?' he added as a question but Karen was too embarrassed to offer any reply even if she had been able to think of one. 'But when it came to the crunch you didn't want to know,' he continued and there was no mistaking either the interest in his voice or the puzzlement. 'It wasn't natural, and I'd like to know just what your idea was?'

'It's difficult to explain,' she returned awkwardly.

'Difficult?' His gaze was fixed and studied. 'That in itself sounds as if there's a hint of mystery about the whole business.'

'Mystery?' she repeated, nerves taut. 'What kind of mystery could there be?'

'Don't adopt an air of innocence,' he rebuked. 'For the success of my particular work I have to be something of a psychologist; I have to study personalities. Yours puzzles me. You'll admit, I hope, that your behaviour last night was so contradictory that you must be a most unusual young woman?' She merely shook her head, unable to find anything to say.

For how could she admit that she had tempted him out of devilment, just to see how he would react? She looked up at him, generously making excuses for his conduct, because what was merely fun to her had appeared as sheer promiscuity to him, and who could blame him? Her quiet reasoning brought forth the conclusion that his reaction was natural; he had not considered it necessary to afford her any respect. It was unfortunate that they had collided on the hotel grounds, and of course he had now accepted that it was not engineered by her after all.

'Aren't you going to give me some sort of an explanation?' he asked, his words cutting into her reverie.

'I can't explain.' There was a hint of distress in her voice, an apologetic expression in the wide stare she gave him. 'It's impossible,' she added finally, turning away, to look for Helen.

'Impossible, eh?' He drew a breath of impatience but he was interested in her, and that interest seemed out of all proportion even before he said, 'What a strange one you are. You're a most unusual and intriguing type—unpredictable, interesting. I'd like to know more about you. Will you dine with me tonight?'

Her eyes widened disbelievingly.

'Are you serious?' she asked.

'I have never been more serious. Perhaps,' he suggested thoughtfully, 'you'd dine with me on my boat? It's moored near here—at the very end of the headland.'

'On your boat?' she repeated and he gave a light laugh.

'Don't worry. I've a housekeeper on board, so you'll be quite safe.

'A housekeeper?' Karen's nerves caught. He had sounded genuine, until the mention of the housekeeper, whose presence would ensure her safety. He knew very well that he had given his housekeeper the day off, and the evening. 'She'll be there this evening?'

'Of course. She'll cook our dinner for us. I shall have to tell her I'm having a guest.' He stopped, his eyes flickering oddly. 'Is anything the matter?' he said puzzled.

'I have my doubts about this housekeeper,' she said lowering her lashes to conceal her expression.

'You don't believe . . . ?' His voice trailed and Karen glanced up to see an expression of amusement on his face. 'Good lord,' he exclaimed. 'I'd forgotten. I've given her the evening off!' He looked ruefully at Karen and a smile broke, causing her to catch her breath at the attractiveness of him. 'What a wolf I'd have appeared if I'd gotten you on my boat and then had to confess that my housekeeper wasn't there after all.'

She laughed then, feeling as if a weight had been lifted from her at the idea that he was genuine, after all.

'This housekeeper,' she was urged to say, 'is she a sort of Girl Friday? That's what they're called, isn't it, when they work on boats?'

'No, this one could not be described as a girl,' he answered in some amusement.

'No?'

'Definitely not.'

'How old is she then?'

He looked at her oddly.

'Is it important?'

'Not really,' she shrugged. 'It was just a matter of interest that made me ask the question, that's all.'

'She says she's forty-five but I'd say she's nearer fifty-five.'

'Fifty-five!' repeated Karen, wide-eyed. 'What makes you say that?'

'The amount of makeup she wears. Trying to look younger than she is. Why women do it I don't know. They'd be much more attractive if they'd grow old gracefully.'

Karen had to laugh, not at what he had just said, but at the idea that he had decided his housekeeper was trying to make herself look *younger!*

'My friend's waiting,' she murmured as she saw

Helen standing some distance away, not wanting to intrude.

'What about my invitation?'

She looked searchingly at him.

'Your girl friend,' she murmured. 'Won't she mind?'

The gray eyes hardened.

'I'm not obliged to obtain anyone's approval for any action I might choose to make,' he said tautly.

'I'm sorry,' she said, feeling like a spanked child.

'You're going to accept my invitation?'

She paused. Did he like her? He had said she was unusual, intriguing, interesting. . . . It did seem that he liked her, she thought, a smile fluttering to her lips as she replied,

'Yes, I'd like to dine with you—' She stopped and he laughed.

'The name's Clint,' he said and that was all.

'Mine's Karen.'

'Karen—what?'

She gave a start, even though she had half expected the question.

'Boyle,' she responded, using her mother's maiden name. 'Where shall we be dining?' she asked. 'It's just that I'd like to know if it's formal?'

'The Sandy Lane—and it is formal tonight. I'll call for you in a taxi—'

'I'd rather meet you there,' she said, her glance flickering to where Helen was still waiting. 'What time? I must join my friend,' she added urgently.

'Eight o'clock, in the lobby.'

Chapter Four

She arrived a quarter of an hour late, having spent rather too long on her appearance. But the result more than pleased her; she knew that the white evening dress suited her to perfection, knew that it was modest and yet seductive, the bodice clinging to her curves as if it had been molded on to them. The silver bracelet and matching ear-drops could not have been bettered as accessories. Her small bag was embroidered with silver thread; her sandals were made of straps of silver leather.

Clint was in the lobby, tall and distinguished as he stood looking down on to the terrace below. His smile was spontaneous when, on seeing her enter, his eyes flickered in appreciation of the enchanting picture she made.

'You look charming,' he said. 'White suits your lovely hair.'

She coloured delicately, disconcerted in a way entirely foreign to her innate confidence.

'Thank you,' she murmured shyly.

'Shall we have a drink on the terrace, or would you prefer the lounge?'

'The terrace sounds nice.'

'Everything's nice about the Sandy Lane,' he assured her. 'It's probably the best hotel in the Caribbean.'

'It's sort—of homey,' Karen was saying a short while later as they had their aperitifs on the flower-bedecked terrace. 'And yet it has the sort of sophistication which people on holiday usually want.'

'I'm glad you like it.' Clint paused a moment, as if considering. 'Tell me about yourself?' he invited. 'I've said I'm intrigued by your behaviour last night. The daring of your challenge to me, a stranger, and then, when it seemed I'd oblige, you backed out—'

'Oh, don't!' she begged, her colour rising. 'Please don't remind me of it!'

'You see what I mean?' He regarded her with an inscrutable expression. 'You're totally unpredictable.'

'I can't explain,' she quivered. 'I've already said so.'

'There must have been some good reason for your behaviour—which, I very soon realised, was completely out of character. Can't you give me that reason?' He seemed inordinately interested, watching her face for any sign of a change of expression. She picked up her glass, taking refuge in silence, and telling herself that it had been a mistake to accept his invitation to dinner. 'So you're not going to talk?' His mouth hardened; he seemed more frustrated than anything else, she thought.

'I'd rather not talk about myself.' She looked apologetically at him.

'Well, don't be so unhappy about it,' he said unexpectedly. 'I've invited you out and it's up to me to see that you enjoy the evening.' He smiled, his ill humour gone. 'Drink up and we'll go and eat.'

Karen fluttered a smile in response, relieved at his change of mood.

They sat in a corner, dining in the open at a table facing the sea, the air around them heavy with the scent of exotic flowers.

They ate huge turtle steaks, juicy and tender as prime veal, and drank champagne to the strains of calypso music drifting up from below, where the steel band was playing in front of a dance area around which white tables and chairs were arranged beneath flowering tropical trees. The blooms of a hibiscus hedge glowed crimson in the reflected light from lamps hidden in the feathery foliage of casuarinas; bougainvillea climbed up a trellis, then tumbled in a riot of magenta and crimson to mingle with a bed of golden allamandas. The sea was dazzling in the moonlight, and the tall palms growing on the backshore waved their delicate spidery fronds against the deep, mysterious purple of a star-sprinkled sky.

Karen sighed, her mind drugged by the sheer magic of her surroundings. It was all so unreal—had been right from the start when she had surely been infected with madness even to think of applying for the post advertised by a man she disliked, a post which necessitated adopting a dual personality. Then there had been the meeting with Clint at Sam Lord's Castle, and her mischievous, unthinking approach which had ended in a way she could never even have visualised. And now, here she was, dining in the exotic atmosphere of this luxury hotel with the man to whom, as his middle-aged housekeeper, she would be serving breakfast at precisely eight o'clock tomorrow morning. It was not only unreal, but incredible. Yet, within seconds she was seeing the amusing side only. After all, she had entered into the masquerade partly for the fun of it, although mainly for the satisfaction, later, of proving to Clint that she really could act.

'Why the sigh?' Clint's voice came softly and she looked at him across the candlelit table.

'I'm drugged by it all,' she answered frankly. 'It's magic, isn't it?'

His dark eyes flickered; Karen had the incredible idea that he was making mental notes of all she did and said, of every gesture and glance, every expression that crossed her face.

'Is that how you regard it—as magic?'

'Yes. The atmosphere affects me profoundly.'

'Any particular reason?'

'There are many reasons.'

'Such as?'

'Well, the very situation we're in—dining here by candlelight, in the open air. And out there the dark sea, so calm, beneath a starlit sky and look at the path the moon's making on the water. It ripples like a stream of silver . . ." Her voice trailed to an embarrassed silence.

'You're a romantic, that's for sure.' Although there was a dash of amusement in his tone his eyes were serious as they looked into hers. 'You mentioned the situation *we* are in. Has the magic anything to do with your companion?'

Karen gave him a startled glance.

'Are you looking for flattery?' she asked.

'I might be. I suppose I'm trying to understand you.'

'I intrigue you, you said?'

'More than that.' He stopped and a baffled expression crossed his face. She had the idea that he was more than a little impatient with himself. But why? And why should he be so interested in her?

She knew instinctively that he intended asking more questions and decided to forestall him.

'Tell me about yourself, Clint. You mentioned something regarding your work—saying you needed to be a psychologist. What's the nature of your work?'

'It wouldn't interest you.' Soft the voice and inflexible. This was a different side to him again, a stern, rather masterful side where the manner he adopted was meant to warn her of the futility of pursuing this particular subject.

'Then tell me about the lady who works for you on your boat?'

He hesitated and she had the firm conviction that although he had no wish to talk about his housekeeper, he at the same time did not want to snub Karen again.

'Miss Waring? There isn't anything interesting about her, I'm afraid.'

'She seems old to be a Girl Friday. Has she been with you long?'

'About six or seven weeks. She wanted a complete change from the routine of her office job and so she answered an advertisement I inserted in a newspaper.'

'She left her job?' with well-feigned surprise. 'She must be adventurous. Usually women of forty-five—Did you say she was older than that?'

'I'd say she's about fifty-five.'

'Women of that age aren't usually adventurous, are they?' Karen stared fixedly at her plate, unable to meet his gaze because of the laughter in her eyes.

'I'd never describe Miss Waring as adventurous,' returned Clint with a touch of humour. 'On the contrary, she's a staid woman, efficient but very reserved.'

'Perhaps she's conscious of her position,' suggested Karen, still avoiding his eyes.

'I don't think so. There's no sense of inferiority with employees these days, and a good thing too.'

Karen did glance up then, rather surprised by what he had said. She had branded him arrogant, full of his own importance, conscious of the place he held in the literary world. . . . Was she mistaken? Her feelings were most illogically mixed, she realised, for while on the one hand she did not want to be mistaken, on the other she was glad that he did not consider as inferior those people who worked for him.

'Is she a good cook?' she was impelled to ask, watching him with a curious expression.

'Quite good, yes. I'm not a fanatic about food anyway. And when I'm working I'm satisfied with plain meals.' He paused a moment, 'Why don't you come on board—perhaps tomorrow evening—and meet her?'

Karen, in the act of putting a piece of turtle steak

into her mouth, almost choked, but managed a swift recovery to say, 'I think she sounds shy, and wouldn't be happy for me to go aboard.'

'I don't suppose she'll take exception to any visitor I might decide to entertain,' he rejoined.

Karen made no answer and for a while they ate in silence, Clint breaking it only to thank the waiter who came unobtrusively to refill their wineglasses.

'Will you let me take you on board, Karen?' Clint broke the silence at last, his voice and manner persuasive.

She shook her head determinedly.

'No—I don't think so. Perhaps some other time,' she added vaguely on seeing him frown.

'You're a strange girl,' he said with a touch of asperity. 'An enigma.'

'Your psychology isn't working,' she said, laughing softly.

'You are quite right,' crisply and with a narrowed look, 'it isn't!'

'You sound angry.' She was enjoying herself but she endeavoured not to let it show. 'What have I done to upset you?'

'The innocent again,' he murmured. 'I wish I knew just what your little game is?'

She shot him a startled glance.

'My little game? That's a strange thing to say!'

'You were up to something last night, and now—well, you are acting damned strange!'

'Just because I won't go on to your boat? It so happens that I don't want to go on to it, and I'm sure I can please myself!'

'It's nothing to do with the boat!'

'What is it then?'

'Your refusal to talk about yourself.' Imperious the tone; Karen felt he would have ordered her to talk about herself if he'd had the power to do so. 'It angers me—' He pulled himself up, frowning darkly as if he realised he had gone too far.

'You are equally reticent,' Karen reminded him quietly. 'We're strangers and in consequence neither has any wish to confide in the other.'

He drew a breath but said, rather to her surprise, 'That's fair enough. I'm sorry if I appeared unfriendly. As I don't want to talk about myself I shouldn't expect you to do so either.'

'Why are you so interested in me?' she queried, eyeing him with an odd expression.

'It doesn't matter,' was his immediate and noncommittal rejoinder.

'It's a case of ships that pass in the night,' she murmured, her ears attuned to the haunting strains of *Yellow Bird* being played by the steel band.

'Ships that pass in the night. . . .' He looked absently at her, then nodded his head. 'Yes, I suppose so.'

He smiled then, his ill humour gone. Karen responded and for the rest of the meal they chatted, mainly about inconsequential things. When it was over, they left the table but stood for a while on the romantically lit terrace. The night was balmy, and through the mothy darkness there drifted the heady perfumes of roses and carnations and the night-scented stocks that abounded in the hotel gardens.

'Shall we dance?' Clint stood looking down at her from his superior height and within her something stirred, vague and too fleeting to grasp. She nodded, unable to help blushing as she recalled that first dance, when she had deliberately tried to flirt with him.

'Yes, I'd like that.'

She was swung into his arms, felt the warmth of his hands through the fine cotton material of her dress, quivered with a new emotion but reasoned logically that any woman must be affected by a man as handsome and distinguished looking as the one partnering her. She danced on air, so well did their steps match, and when presently she glanced around she saw that all the people at the tables were watching them. A few minutes before the music stopped, she and Clint were the only couple dancing and every eye was on them. When the music did stop and they walked from the floor to their table Clint's hand stayed round her waist, almost possessively.

They danced several more times and then walked along the talcum-soft sands of the beach, a starlit sky above and the moon-drenched sea stretching away to the indistinct line where it melted into the arc of the sky. Music could still be heard—soft strains and a little sad, haunting, like the whisper of a night breeze rustling pine needles on a lonely hillside. It seemed natural that Clint should lead her gently toward the trees, and when he stopped she looked up, her eyes dreamy and luminous as they watched the moon glide through a lacy film of cloud, only to reappear in all its argent glory, flaring, flooding the silent world with romance. Clint, looking down into her lovely face, seemed fascinated by its perfection, and a long, profound moment passed before he drew her slender body to him. There was bliss in the touch of his hands and heaven in his kiss; it was a heady draught dissolving all inhibitions, all restraint. Karen had no power of resistance. Her strong and eager arms slid around him, and with a little exclamation that could have been surprise he swept her into an embrace that was almost as savage as that first one, but now there was respect, and the pain inflicted by his iron-hard body was unintentional. The blood surged in Karen's veins, rushing to her heart in a wild, overflowing sensation that was heightened by the magical setting of moon-pale sands and silvered sea, by the intoxicating fragrance of flowers carried on the zephyr of a breeze making music in the waving palms above their heads.

'You're . . . beautiful. . . .' Clint's voice was a throaty bass tone, his lips probingly insistent as they forced hers apart, his arms almost cruel in their strength as they caused her body to arch so that she was masterfully compelled to experience the sensual throbbing of his iron-hard muscles, the insistent virility of his loins. She tried to resist his demanding mouth when it sought the rounded firmness of her breast but sanity seemed to be fast deserting her. Ecstasy vibrated through her body as Clint awakened emotions she had never before experienced. She had the hazy recollection of saying, only a couple of hours ago, that Clint and she were strangers. . . . And now they were on the very brink of intimacy; she was forced to submission when his hard possessive mouth insisted that she offer him the sweet moisture of hers, she was compelled to respond to his body's erotic rhythm, know the pleasure-pain of roving hands that were as ruthless as they were gentle. The breath in her throat seemed almost to solidify, choking her.

It was only when his hand slid from her waist and then lower that some modicum of sanity returned and, taking him by surprise, she wrested her body from his crushing embrace, to stand, gasping for air, her breasts rising and falling as her heightened emotions still held her in their grip.

Karen had no idea what she expected as a result of her urgent need to escape, but Clint just stood there, regarding her in the moonlight, and he might almost have been mentally recording every sign of emotion—the breathless movements of her body, the clenched fist at her sides, the anxious question in her eyes, asking what he thought of her loss of restraint after her violent repulsion of him only twenty-four hours earlier. She saw his jaw flex, his eyes narrow as a frown knit his brow. He seemed strangely at a loss and she would have given much to know what his thoughts were. One thing was for sure: his ardour had cooled and she knew she had nothing to fear regarding a renewal of his advances. She released a long breath, alive to the fact that although relief was her chief emotion, there was a sense of loss within her, a yearning that most certainly should not have been there.

'Shall we go back, Karen?' His words came like an icy shower, so cold and unemotional was the tone in which they were spoken. She could have burst into tears of mortification, so ashamed did she feel. The incident meant nothing to him; she was a stranger still. And yet, what else could she be? She pulled herself together, casting off her humiliation and attempted to act with the same coolness as he. To her surprise she succeeded, but felt that he must now be condemning her as a no-good, while at the same time still puzzled by her furious response to his advances last night.

He wanted to take her home but she said she would get a taxi, at which he shrugged carelessly and, going to the desk, asked the hall porter to get one for her.

'Good night,' she said, a quiver in her voice despite her previous success at hiding her feelings.

'Good night, Karen. Sleep well.'

Good night . . . and goodbye. . . . That was what he was really saying. . . .

How could she have acted with what could only be described as promiscuity? What must he think of her? Yet, did it matter? She had slipped, but she was philosophical enough to accept that it would have happened one day. The awakening was inevitable and if it had not been Clint who had been responsible it would have been some other man. She now knew the passions, the desires of her body and it was up to her to be guarded in the future. No more risks of that kind—at least, not until she met the man she wanted to marry. It would be very different then.

Chapter Five

Three days had gone by since the evening Clint had taken Karen to the Sandy Lane, and only now was she fully recovered from the experience of his lovemaking. As she had said to Helen, she was beginning to find difficulty in alienating her real self from the character she had assumed. And after that experience she had found it even more difficult, although she had at last succeeded.

It had seemed so simple at the time she had embarked upon the escapade; all she had considered was her expertise in the art of disguise. In no way had she envisaged a situation where she would meet Clint Fraser as anyone other than the middle-aged housekeeper she was supposed to be. Well, it had turned out very differently, and all because of her impulsive action in going up to him and making him dance with her at Sam Lord's Castle, an action done with the anticipation of adding to his chagrin when eventually the unmasking took place.

However, by the time three days had gone by Karen had for the most part managed to forget her real self when on the boat, and to her relief any slight awkwardness she had felt on the morning following the incident had escaped her employer's notice. She felt sure he believed her to be slightly eccentric anyway, so even if she did stammer or appear awkward he would not attach any importance to it.

On the fourth morning, having cooked Clint's breakfast, Karen carried it into the dining saloon where he was waiting, as usual. He had become rather more affable toward her recently, the brief greetings morning and evening having developed to small conversations, and so she had no hesitation about saying,

'You've been working very hard these past three days, Mr. Fraser, so obviously your play's coming along well. You got over your difficulty, apparently?'

'I did get over it, yes, and as you say, I've been able to do a great deal of work during the past three days, but—' He shook his head, a frown on his brow. 'I'm afraid I'm at a standstill again,' he admitted.

'That's a shame,' she commiserated. 'Is it your heroine again?'

He nodded immediately and his frown deepened.

'I've never tried to create a heroine quite like this one—' He stopped, a slow smile dawning. 'I mustn't bore you, Miss Waring. You can't be interested in the problems of a playwright.'

'I am interested,' she assured him. 'I—er—used to know someone who was an actress.'

'You did? Who was she?'

'Oh, no one you'd know,' she said airily. 'She was only an amateur.'

'Amateurs can sometimes be good,' he said, and Karen lowered her head to hide the smile that came to her lips. Yes, amateurs could sometimes be good . . . and one day, Mr. Clint Fraser, you will know just how good!

'We were talking about your play,' she reminded him presently, 'and you were saying your heroine was giving you trouble again?'

'I seem to have run out of ideas regarding her; she wasn't giving me trouble until yesterday afternoon, when I suddenly realised that I could not envisage the way she would react to a certain situation.'

Karen looked sympathetic.

'Perhaps I can help?' she offered. 'What is the situation?'

Clint looked at her thoughtfully and said nothing for a space; Karen had the impression that he was seriously considering her suggestion. His next words confirmed this.

'She's a lot younger than you, Miss Waring.'

Karen's lashes came down, hiding her expression.

'I expected she would be,' she returned at length. 'However, I do happen to have been young once, Mr. Fraser,' she added nostalgically. 'I believe I still know what the feelings of a young woman are.'

'Of course,' he agreed kindly, but went on to add that he didn't think she would have ever been anything like his heroine.

'No?' Karen was looking down at the toe of her serviceable black shoe, scarcely able to suppress laughter. 'Is she so different, then?'

'Yes, she is, but I *wanted* her to be different. The modern girl today follows a pattern and when you've met one you've met the lot—'

'Oh, I can't agree—!' Karen stopped, aghast that in her indignation she had dropped her assumed voice, although only for a fleeting second.

'You don't agree?' He was looking oddly at her, but to her intense relief he seemed not to have noticed her slip, which was, after all, only a minor one. 'Perhaps not in your day, Miss Waring, but today—' He shook his head. 'I find the average young woman affected, arch, and more often than not, boring. Hence my desire to create a female who is different, one who is—exciting, interesting. I want the hero to be intrigued by her, unable to know what she is likely to do next.'

'I see. . . .' Karen gave a small sigh. 'I don't think I can help you, then,' she said apologetically.

He smiled at her and said soothingly, 'Don't look so forlorn about it, Miss Waring. I shall overcome my difficulty; I had to do it before.'

'Well, I wish you luck,' she smiled and left him to his breakfast.

Helen had not left the bungalow when she arrived there.

'I thought I'd do my washing,' she said, grimacing at Karen's drab appearance. 'I want to take a snapshot of you in that getup,' she decided. 'We can then have a good laugh in the years to come!'

'I don't think I'd want to look at this again!' Karen was in front of a long mirror in the living room of the bungalow. 'To tell you the truth, Helen, I wish it was all over and I could look around for another post.'

'You're intending to stay here?' Helen was listening for the washing machine to stop.

'Yes; at least for as long as Jean stays. It seems all wrong that there should be thousands of miles distance between us.'

'I agree—but we shall all miss you. What will you do with your flat? It's your own property, isn't it?'

'Well, it's mortgaged. I might keep it on or I might sell it. I haven't made up my mind.' She paused, then said she would go and get rid of her disguise.

'I'll have some coffee ready when you've finished.'

They sat on the patio drinking it, watching the para-gliders with their brightly coloured parachutes, having fun in the smooth, aquamarine water. The sun was high, spangling the sea with diamonds; children were playing beach ball with their parents; others were flying gaily coloured kites. Elderly men and women were taking life easy beneath the protection of gaudy beach umbrellas. It was a gay scene but an uncrowded one, with tall coconut palms against the sky, and the delicate foliage of casuarinas waving gently, allowing golden shafts of sunshine to create a tapestry of light and shade on the pearl-white sands of the beach. Several red-sailed yachts glided along languidly just offshore, and through it all there was laughter and chatter, and the lilting melody of *This is my Island in the Sun* being played by a strolling minstrel with a guitar.

'I've some shopping to do for Mr. Fraser,' Karen said when Helen, having finished her washing and hung it out on the patio, was ready for the beach. 'Perhaps we'll go into Bridgetown after lunch?'

'Yes, I'd like that. I've been wanting to buy some souvenirs. If I get them today they'll be done with.' She paused a moment. 'Are you off this evening?'

'No, I've to be back on the boat by half-past seven.'

'I've made another date with Bill. It's their last day today; they fly home tomorrow.' A small sigh and then, 'I've had over a week already. Why does the time go so quickly?'

'Don't think about it,' pleaded Karen. 'You've almost two weeks yet. I don't know what I shall do when you've gone. As you know, Jean won't be back for at least another two months.'

'Does your boss know that his housekeeper's sister's away?' inquired Helen with interest.

'Yes.'

'Does he know where she lives?'

'Yes. He did ask me that, so I told him.'

Helen said nothing, merely picking up her beach bag, and a new bottle of suntan lotion that stood on the table.

The capital was a charming, bustling city where could be seen the spectacle of West Indian life in all its varied aspects. The two girls made for Broad Street, and the modern department stores where Helen bought French perfume and some embroidered cloth and several lengths of batik.

'I want the chemists,' Karen said when they came out. 'It's on the corner of Swan Street.'

'Won't any chemist do?'

'I suppose so, but Mr. Fraser told me to go to that one, so I had better do so.'

Karen wanted a certain brand of after-shave lotion, a tube of toothpaste, toilet soap and a nail brush. The shop was small but well-stocked, and Karen was soon served and coming away, having chatted for a few moments with the English proprietor.

They then took a taxi along Highway Three to spend a pleasant afternoon at Andromeda Gardens, one of the loveliest places in the whole of the island, where a stream cascaded over the massive limestone boulders which, rising to many and varied levels, formed the most unusual and fantastic setting for exotic flowers like heliconiums and oleanders, bougainvillea and hibiscus, ferns and palms and a myriad other subtropical and sweet smelling flowers. They were fortunate because the owner, the lady who started it all with the intention of giving it to the nation, just happened to be wandering around and they chatted with her for most of the afternoon.

'You exhibit at Chelsea, don't you?' said Karen, delighting the owner with her knowledge. 'I saw your stand this year, when I was there. Were you there?'

'No, unfortunately I couldn't go, but I'm delighted that our exhibits gave you so much pleasure.'

Karen and Helen came away feeling well satisfied with their afternoon out, and they put a nice finish to it by having tea on the shady patio of the bungalow, enjoying the now familiar spectacle of the glorious beach and the tranquil sapphire sea where the most interesting sight of the moment was that of the surf riders.

'Well, I must be getting ready to go,' sighed Karen. 'All good things come to an end. Have a nice evening with Bill.'

'We're going to the Pepper-pot to see the Merry-men.'

'What about Derek? Has he got himself a girl friend?'

Helen nodded.

'Yes, but she's not what I'd call the sociable type. Bill and I wanted them to make a foursome, but she seems to want to be alone with Derek.'

Karen shrugged but made no comment.

Helen came to the bedroom door when she was changing.

'Can I come in?'

'Of course.' Having taken off her sundress, Karen was in her bra and panties, her beautiful tan lending even more allure to a figure that was as near perfect as any figure could be.

She had the gray dress in her hand and a laugh escaped Helen as she said, 'You wear those—beneath that drab getup?'

'Well, you needn't look so surprised,' laughed Karen. 'There's no reason in the world why I should have to wear a chemise and bloomers, is there?'

'No, I suppose not . . . but they're so incongruous, those dainty bits of lace beneath that dress you're putting on.'

Karen slipped it over her head; its folds fell down to about six inches above her ankles. Her stockings were black, her shoes highly polished. She grimaced and said she was not sure that she hadn't overdone it.

'Mr. Fraser thinks I look fifty-five.'

Helen's eyes widened.

'He actually told you that?'

'I asked him about his housekeeper—'

'You did?' incredulously. 'Really, Karen, you were taking a risk, surely! How could you keep a straight face when he was talking about you—her—oh, lord, you know what I mean!'

Karen's eyes were glistening with humour.

'It was fun. He said she was trying to make herself look younger by the use of cosmetics, and he wondered why women could not grow old gracefully.'

Helen subsided into laughter.

'How the devil did you keep a straight face?' she asked when she had recovered.

'It was difficult,' answered Karen reflectively. 'It needed all my experience of acting, I can tell you.'

'I'll bet it did!' Helen paused, looking her over. The makeup was complete and Karen was pushing her lovely dark hair beneath the dry grayness of the wig. The glasses completed the transformation and Helen gave a low whistle.

'I know I've said it before—every time you do it, in fact—but I'm saying it again. You're an expert, Karen, and if ever you become a fugitive from justice they'll never catch you.'

Karen merely smiled, and with one last look in the mirror she said she must be on her way.

Helen accompanied her to the front door and just as she opened it an elderly gentleman happened to be passing and for no apparent reason he stopped dead on seeing Karen. Then, looking rather sheepish, he walked on, a gray-haired man of medium height and build, and a slight droop to his shoulders. He was a few yards in front of her as she followed the path leading from the Vervain Hotel to a place where she could enter the grounds of the Smuggler's Cove Hotel. And it was just at that point that he happened to turn, and again stopped.

Frowning, Karen carried on, increasing her pace, but as she came abreast of him he said, 'Excuse me speaking to you, but I've seen you several times, and I thought I would like to introduce myself. I'm George Lawson, a widower.' He smiled benignly at her and waited for her response.

'Oh—er—well, I'm pleased to make your acquaintance, Mr. Lawson,' she said nonplused.

'I'm here for two months,' he offered eagerly. 'I've been ill and as I'd saved a bit I thought I'd recuperate here, in the sun. Gertrude, my married daughter, was here with her husband last year and they recommended it. But it's lonely. . .' His voice trailed shyly. 'You seem to be on your own too, and I thought—well—that you and I, that we— Are you on holiday as well?' he asked, dragging out a handkerchief to mop his brow. 'I'd like to keep company with you.'

Karen, laughter bubbling up inside her, had to turn away because she had the utmost difficulty suppressing it. However, quite unable to be unkind to the man, she said gently, 'I'm sorry, but I'm not on holiday. I have work to do. But in any case I wouldn't want to keep company with you.'

'Work?' he slanted her a surprised glance. 'I've seen you about often—'

'I'm sorry,' she repeated, then stopped, becoming conscious of a firm and insistent step behind her and she automatically moved to one side.

'Thank you, Miss Waring,' said her employer politely. And his eyes, faintly satirical, moved from her face to that of the man who had also stepped aside.

Although colouring beneath her makeup, aware as she was that Clint Fraser had overheard much of what George Lawson was saying, she nevertheless felt the whole situation was fast becoming hilarious. Laughter bubbled up inside her again to reach aching proportions in her efforts to suppress it.

'Will you think about it?' asked the old man persuasively. 'I'm not short of money, so I could take you about a bit.'

'No thank you,' she said firmly. 'I have no wish to go out with anyone.'

'But you're on your own,' he persisted. 'I . . . like you.' He looked sheepishly at her. 'We could do very nicely together.'

'I'm sure you'll find a suitable companion, Mr. Lawson.' Karen increased her pace, hoping he would not attempt to keep up with her but she was disappointed. He accompanied her right to the boat, so she had to stop and say, 'Look, I work on this boat. The gentleman who spoke to me owns it and I'm his housekeeper. My time's occupied. Good afternoon, Mr. Lawson,' she added and, in her hurry to get away, forgot her role and ran swiftly up the gangway only to collide with her employer who happened to appear from nowhere as she reached the top.

He had caught her by the arms to steady her, staring in surprise at the speed with which she had been running. His eyes strayed to the man looking up at them; and his fine lips quivered with amusement.

'You appear to have found yourself a gentleman

friend, Miss Waring,' he commented dryly. 'Why do you run from him? He seems very inoffensive to me.'

'Mr. Fraser,' she quivered, 'I do not want to have anything whatsoever to do with him!'

'Fair enough. I shall endeavour to get rid of him for you, once and for all.' Releasing her, he turned, beckoning. 'Come here, my man,' he ordered, and without hesitation he obeyed. 'Now, might I ask what you mean by molesting my housekeeper?'

'Well, sir—I sort of—like her, if you know what I mean?'

By this time Karen, her little spurt of anger dissolved by her mirth, had turned away, her shoulders heaving, to escape to her cabin, tears of laughter rolling down her face.

'What the deuce of a pickle!' she laughed. 'Wait until I tell Helen tomorrow. Her sides'll ache with laughing!'

'I believe I've managed to put your amorous suitor off,' Clint assured her a little later. 'But it's obvious that he's fallen in love with you—'

'Rubbish, Mr. Fraser. Please say no more about it!' She was acting the outraged spinster, indignantly refusing to listen. 'I'm not interested in men!'

As it was a little too early to begin preparing the dinner Karen decided to wash her underwear. She had just finished and was shaking them out ready to hang in her bathroom, when suddenly the door to the galley opened and her employer stood there, his gray eyes widening as they moved from the lacy scrap she held in her hand to the matching bra lying by the sink. Never had Karen been more thankful for the greasepaint covering that effectively hid her blushes.

Clint appeared to make a swift recovery from his surprise, but there was certainly an odd expression on his face as he looked at her, while she was so disconcerted that she found herself speaking first, stammering out words that would have been better left unsaid.

'Oh—Mr. Fraser! You've—never come in—here before at this time! I—I—never expected you. . . .

The gray eyes wandered back to the garment in her hand; she screwed it up into a tiny ball, belatedly trying to hide it from his view. She saw his glance rove over her and, as once before, she had the sensation of being stripped. Her figure in the unshapely, loose fitting dress seemed far larger than the sort of figure for which the bra and panties were designed.

'I came merely to tell you I'd not be having dinner this evening. I should have told you this morning but I didn't know then that I wouldn't be able to work.'

'It's still not going right?' Karen said, making a tremendous effort to regain her composure even while knowing it was quite impossible with that bit of lace lying there, and the other screwed up in her hand, its dainty trimming visible in spite of her efforts to conceal it.

'No, Miss Waring, it isn't going right. I shall get myself some recreation by dining out this evening.' He looked oddly at her before turning away. She watched the door close, then her innate sense of humour prevailed and she shook with silent laughter.

What should she do with herself? Neither the thought of spending the evening alone on the boat nor in the bungalow appealed, and she suddenly remembered Bill and Derek highly recommending the Tamarind Cove Hotel for dinner and she decided to try it, remembering too that there was a very special entertainment this evening which had been advertised in the Vervain Hotel. It was late to try and book a table but she might just be lucky.

She rang from the Vervain before going to the bungalow to change and to her intense satisfaction was able to reserve a table for one.

Helen had not yet left the bungalow when Karen arrived, and as there were a few minutes to spare. Karen—after telling her that she had the evening off—related the story about the old man, and for a few uncontrollable seconds Helen was speechless with laughter. Her eyes were actually moist when at last she was able to say, 'This gets more and more entertaining every minute! And your boss had to get rid of him, you say?'

'Yes, that's right. He was obviously highly amused, and said he thought the man had fallen in love with me.'

Helen went into another peal of laughter and Karen scarcely let her recover when she related the incident of the underwear.

'I didn't know where to put myself,' she added. 'I searched for something to say—for some explanation but it was impossible. . . .' Her voice trailed as Helen's laughter rang out through the room again, her whole body affected by mirth.

'Did he say anything?' she wanted to know when eventually she had regained her calm.

'Naturally he didn't. What could he say? He looked me over,' went on Karen before Helen could speak, 'as if he were trying to see exactly what I had on beneath my dress.'

'Oh Karen,' cried Helen collapsing into a chair, 'you're going into this deeper and deeper!'

'Why am I?' casually and with a shrug of her shoulders. 'I was disconcerted at first, and I suppose I shall feel strange tomorrow morning when I serve his breakfast, but as he can't very well introduce the subject of his housekeeper's underwear I've really nothing to worry about.'

'Until the end . . . and the showdown,' Helen reminded her darkly.

Karen laughed, eyes sparkling. But she said nothing, wanting only to get rid of her disguise. Helen was concerned about her spending the evening on her own but Karen reassured her by the information that she had managed to book a table at the Tamarind Cove Hotel where a special entertainment was to be put on this evening.

'There's a famous steel band and calypso singers, and also two very famous limbo dancers. I'm really looking forward to it, Helen, so please don't worry about me.'

'Well . . . if it's what you want. But you could join Bill and me if you'd like to?'

'And play gooseberry?' with a lift of her brows. 'No; but thank you all the same '

After discarding the wig and cleaning the greasepaint off, Karen had a bath and put on an ankle length dress of coral-coloured chiffon, which she had been tempted to buy in the shop at the Smuggler's Cove Hotel. Full-skirted and nipped in at the waist, it had a high, mandarin collar and long, very full sleeves gathered in to a tight cuff. The bodice at the back was slit from neck to waist. Her hair, newly washed that morning, gleamed when she brushed it, highlighted with tawny-gold, forming an enchanting halo for a face of exquisite beauty. A quarter of an hour later she was in a taxi on her way to the hotel.

Chapter Six

The setting for the evening's special entertainment was the long broad terrace, the tables being placed around the area where the floor show was to take place. On each table a candle flickered from its crimson jar, spreading a romantic, subdued light on to the cloth and the gleaming silver and glass. Surrounding the terrace tall lamps with naked flares set an added scene for an evening of dining and dancing and typical West Indian entertainment. The whole atmosphere was gay, with chatter and laughter and with the steel band playing for those people who had already begun to dine. Karen had been shown to her table, which to her delight was right at the front, opposite the band, when another waiter approached and a whispered conversation went on between him and the waiter who had shown Karen to her table. She caught the words. '. . but it was booked this afternoon—'

'This lady has the table,' from the waiter, almost angrily.

At last they both turned, their expressions troubled and apologetic.

'There has been some mistake,' the first waiter said. 'This table was booked by a gentleman this afternoon.'

'Oh. . . .' Karen rose to her feet, embarrassed by the stares of people at nearby tables. 'I booked it later, so. . . .' She spread her hands and lifted her evening bag from the back of the chair where she had hung it. 'You have another table?' She was disappointed because she felt she would not be given a table so near to the front as this one was.

'That's the trouble,' apologised the waiter, 'we're fully booked because this is a special night, with famous people entertaining. It's not often that we make a mistake and I can only say I am very sorry. The other waiter did ask the gentleman to share his table with you but he refused.'

She smiled reassuringly at him, noting how impressive he looked in the immaculate white linen that contrasted so attractively with his shining mahogany skin.

'It isn't your fault, so please don't look so worried about it. I'll go somewhere else.' She had turned to make her way back to the steps leading to the exit when she saw the second waiter coming toward her, followed by the man who had booked the table. Karen gave a gasp as she saw who it was. The waiter turned.

'Karen!' There was no mistaking the pleasure on Clint's face, and swiftly she recalled his coldness as he left her on that previous occasion. Why, then, was he so glad to see her now? 'But this is wonderful! You're dining here this evening?'

'This is the lady, sir, who was occupying your table.'

'This—? We shall share it,' he said decisively without asking her. 'I had no idea this was the lady who had my table or I'd have told you I didn't mind sharing.'

Both waiters, all smiles now, inclined their heads and the first, after seeing them seated, went off to collect what was necessary for laying the second cover.

'Thank you,' said Karen demurely. She had coloured delicately, her eyes lowered, for she was recalling vividly the last time they had been together. 'It was kind of you to offer to share your table with me. I was quite disappointed at the thought of not seeing the show.'

'It'll be very good.' His gray eyes were focused on her face and she felt as if she were being compelled to look up and meet his scrutiny. What a strange coincidence that they should meet again. There were so many luxury hotels where he could have dined but she supposed that he, like she, had chosen the Tamarind Cove because of the special entertainment.

'I'm glad we met again,' said Clint when the waiter, having laid the cover and left the menu, went away again. 'I've been thinking a lot about you since we were last together.'

She frowned and shook her head, silently begging him not to remind her of it, but his reassuring smile appeared instantly, as if he were anxious to save her embarrassment.

'It's a coincidence that we're both here,' she murmured, more for something to say than anything else. And then she just had to ask, 'How do you come to be alone, though? Your girl friend . . . it's serious?'

'It could be. Neither of us is in a hurry though.'

A slight heaviness seemed to descend upon Karen's spirits.

'Does she live here?'

'No, on Grenada. She and some friends of hers happen to be holidaying here.' That was all; obviously he had no intention of talking about his girl friend.

But Karen, compelled by some force out of her control, persisted, 'Why aren't you with her this evening?'

'She's with her friends and I had no wish to join them.' Rigid the voice suddenly, inexorable; Karen saw a matching inflexibility in his eyes and knew that if she were to avoid a snub she must refrain from questioning him further.

She asked instead, 'Why have you been thinking about me since we last met?' He had not wanted to make another date, she recalled, but of course that was understandable, his having a girl friend with whom he appeared to be going steady.

'Because you puzzle me,' he began, when she interrupted him.

'You've said that before. I'm a very ordinary person, really—when you get to know me.' Her eyes looked beyond him to the cascading showers of a bougainvillea vine on a trellis to one side of which the steel band was playing.

'Ordinary?' with a lift of his brows. 'No such thing!

You're a most *extraordinary* young lady.' He paused as if taking special care about framing his next words. 'I must know, Karen, why, after repulsing me one evening, you were willing the next?'

She coloured, and shot him a resentful glance.

'Please. . . . It isn't gentlemanly to remind me of it!'

'I'm not intentionally being anything other than a gentleman,' he denied. 'I've absolutely nothing against you for your delightful reciprocation. It was a revelation to me.'

She stared, as if expecting him to expand on that but he, too, was waiting and after only the slightest hesitation she said, frankly, 'On the second occasion there were romantic preliminaries—the hotel, which you yourself declared to be something quite exceptional—the dining by candlelight, tbe dancing to the steel band . . . oh, and so much else besides!'

Clint's gray eyes had become dark and keen with interest. He seemed avid for more as he said, 'So that was the difference—and the result?'

'Yes, it was.'

'You've had the same experience before obviously, you're too beautiful not to have had—'

'No, I've never had that kind of experience before.'

Silence—the silence of disbelief. Clint's eyes widened, then narrowed inscrutably.

'You don't believe me?' A spark of hostility lit Karen's eyes, the result of an upsurge of anger at his manner. 'I don't care whether you do or not!'

His expression changed on the instant.

'I do believe you,' he assured her quietly. 'Yes, Karen, I couldn't do otherwise with that kind of indignation in your eyes.'

Somewhat mollified, she managed to respond to the persuasive smile he gave her.

'Let's see what we shall order,' he suggested, and for the next few minutes they pored over the menu, both choosing the same in the end—a starter of cold soup flavoured with garlic and peppers, then a seafood collection including lobster and scallops served in a delicious brandy, sherry and cheese sauce.

'And wine?' Clint smiled at her across the candlelit table. 'Shall we have champagne?'

'Yes, please. It's my favourite drink.' She was thinking that she had come here alone expecting to pay for herself. She would still like to do just that but was very much afraid Clint would resent even the merest suggestion that she pay for her own dinner.

'Oh, but this is marvelous!' the exclamation leaped to Karen's lips after the limbo dancers had performed their incredible act. 'How do they do it?'

Clint, watching her every change of expression, gave no immediate reply and, as once before, Karen had the idea that he was making mental notes.

'You mean, you haven't seen limbo dancers before?' he inquired strangely.

'Not as good as these,' she answered guardedly.

The gray eyes flickered. There was no doubt in her mind that he was exceedingly curious about her but, as he was disinclined to talk about his affairs she was safe; he would not expect her to do what he himself was unwilling to do. And yet, what an unusual situation they were in! Not that it mattered, for they might never meet again after tonight.

During the intervals in the floor show Karen and Clint chatted, and she could not help but be conscious of the admiration in his gaze, which seemed to be taking in every single thing about her face—and often it would become fixed on some feature—her eyes, her mouth or, as now, on the faint thread of blue transparency at her temple. A smile broke from her lips, to be mirrored in her eyes. He leaned back in his chair as if being forced to relax, in order to fully appreciate what he was seeing. He appeared to be satisfied about something and she was puzzled. But the moment passed and the calypso singers came on. After the performance there was another interval and Clint asked Karen to dance. She trod on air, floating on a magic carpet to a realm called Paradise.

Her happiness showed, as it was bound to do. She shone up at him and heard him catch his breath. Was he beginning to like her . . . in *that* way? Impossible. Besides, there was his girl friend. But he had not been very enthusiastic when he had spoken about her, Karen reflected.

She was still thinking about the girl when he led her back to the table but she soon thrust the unwanted picture from her mind, pretending the girl did not even exist.

'I'm feeling rather guilty,' she heard her companion say and glanced up to look interrogatingly at him.

'Why?'

'It's Miss Waring, my Girl Friday as you call her. I forgot to tell her I wouldn't be in for dinner and she came back to get it ready.'

'Came back from where?' Karen could not resist asking.

'She spends a good deal of her time at her sister's bungalow.'

'Her sister lives here, on the island?'

'Yes; she works at the Vervain Hotel and lives in one of the bungalows. But she's away at present and Miss Waring must be lonely, on her own in the bungalow all day.'

'You don't need her during the day?'

'No, there isn't much for her to do at all.' His voice had changed to abruptness and it was plain that he was regretting having mentioned his housekeeper.

But Karen was tempted again and she said, her eyes moving away from his, 'What does she do with her time, then?'

'She says she reads. It's a dull life for her, I'm thinking, but it's partly her own fault, since she's obviously never been interested in marriage.' He paused, his lips quivering with sudden mirth. 'She could have had a beau today. An elderly gentleman wanted to take her out.'

Karen's eyes widened in simulated interest.

'You saw him?'

'Yes. As a matter of fact I had to get rid of him for her. I'd like you to meet Miss Waring, Karen, and give me your opinion of her.'

She flashed him a startled glance.

'Why—er—any particular reason?'

He hesitated, frowning in thought.

'She's beginning to puzzle me—' He stopped abruptly and Karen had the greatest difficulty in hiding her amusement. For it was plain that the thought now in his mind was of those dainty undies his housekeeper was washing.

'In what way?' she persisted, wondering if he would

reveal what was in his mind. But he was already shaking his head.

'It doesn't matter,' he returned casually, and changed the subject.

Karen looked at him, and although admiring him for his reticence, she could not help but be a little disappointed, feeling that if he had talked she would have had something exceedingly amusing to relate to her friend when she saw her the following day.

'You look very happy,' Clint was saying when at last the floor show was over. 'You've enjoyed the evening apparently?'

'Very much—and thank you for everything.'

'Don't thank me, Karen,' he protested gently. 'I've had a most enjoyable evening.'

She fluttered him a lovely smile, convinced that she would never be quite the same after tonight. The romance of the setting and the Caribbean entertainment; and for her partner a man so handsome and distinguished looking that women of all ages were surreptitiously casting glances toward the table at which he sat. Typically feminine, Karen naturally felt proud to be his chosen companion, and the envy of her sex.

'Are you ready to go?' Clint's voice cut into her train of thought and she gave a little sigh.

People around them were moving; tables were being cleared, candles blown out.

'I feel so sad now, Clint.' The words came from nowhere. Karen had had no intention of saying anything like that.

'Because a lovely evening's coming to an end?'

Clint's voice was gentle to her ears, his smile almost tender. The nerves around her heart fluttered, then stilled, only to begin all over again when she saw the expression in his eyes.

'Because a lovely evening *is* at an end,' she corrected, with another little sigh.

'It needn't be,' he said softly. 'Come for a walk along the beach with me.' He was at her side; she caught the tempting male smell of him, felt the touch of his hand beneath her elbow, and it needed no added persuasion to bring her to her feet and come up beside him. But yet she hesitated.

'I. . . .' She glanced at him appealingly. 'Perhaps I'd better be—be going. . . .'

A low laugh escaped him, and she thought how very different he was from that aloof and distant playwright who had disparaged her acting.

'It's early yet,' Clint slid an arm about her waist and she let him take her out into the scintillating, starlit night, where her mind lost itself in a delightful mist of reverie as she relived the pleasures of the past couple of hours. Clint led her through gardens where the air was balmy with the fragrance of magnolias drifting on the northeast trade wind breeze, and then beyond the grounds to the moon-spangled beach. Not another person to be seen, not a murmur other than the sound of the breeze in the foliage on the towering dome palms fringing the shore. Clint urged her toward the shelter of some casuarina trees and took her in his arms. It was so natural that she should be there, so right that he should be looking at her in that masterful way, one hand caressing her cheek and her throat before his fingers explored the nape of her neck and slid into the silken halo of her hair. A thrill shot through her and an ache of sheer pleasure caught her throat. Nerve fibers quivered, tiny vibrations shooting through her body, tingles of rapturous expectation. Clint's eyes lit with a sort of tender amusement just seconds before he bent his head to kiss her. There was rapture in his embrace, the thrill of ecstasy in the male moisture of his lips sliding over hers—a stimulating prelude to a kiss that was as savage as it was tender. Already drugged by the romance of the evening, and this moon-pale setting, Karen knew the vital force of idealistic desire—nothing sensual, yet with heaven no more than a breath away.

She quickened to the caress of his tongue probing the depths of her mouth, thrilled to the questing warmth of his palm as it slid into the opening at the back of her dress to explore the soft flesh over her ribs and seek the rounded firmness of her breast.

'You're so different,' he whispered, and Karen was reminded of what he had said to his housekeeper about all modern girls being alike. But *she* was different in his eyes. . . .

He held her from him; the moon sailing through a lacy gauze of cirrus clouds cast shadows on his lean, angular features, hardening them, but the floating silver disc was full again in all its glorious light and the impression was gone as swiftly as it came. The moon seemed low and close, while the stars, like powdered diamonds, receded. The overhanging branches of the trees were painted silver, beautiful and bizarre.

'Tell me, Karen, what are you thinking?' Clint's

whispered words were music in her ears, his breath against her cheek the pure caress of a breeze at dawn.

'It's . . . romantic,' she answered, peace flowing over her so that she relaxed within the haven of his arms.

'Romantic. . . . Tell me, what is your definition of romance?'

'Stardust and dreams—' The words slipped out, from somewhere in her subconscious; she was as surprised as he when they were uttered.

'Stardust and dreams. . . .' His murmuring repetition seemed to be made so that he would retain the words. 'Not reality, then?' Karen could find no answer simply because she did not know to what it related. His next words enlightened her. 'What about sex? Is that not reality? You believe that sex is in the mind first and then in the body?'

'I believe that true love is spiritual first, and that the fulfillment is physical.' She looked at him in the moonlight, a smile stealing hesitantly to her lips. 'You think I'm silly, don't you?'

He shook his head.

'On the contrary. I'm of the opinion that you're a most extraordinary girl. Haven't I said so?' He smiled down at her and everything about him was tender until she put her arms around his neck, her fingers relishing the impression of strength at the nape. She heard Clint's swift intake of breath, and every nerve in her body responded when he swept her into his arms, crushing her to him, kissing her passionately on the mouth, the throat, the vulnerable places behind her ear. His fingers teased until her nipples hardened to desire, and in a great upsurge of longing she arched her body to the coiled-spring inflexibility of his Little moans of ecstasy escaped her as she strove to come even closer to the taut muscles of his loins One of Clint's hands moved with slow intimacy to her lower body, pressing her to him as if he too, could not get close enough. How she wanted him! If only she and he were alone in that primordial isolation of a world just born, free of inhibitions and the reins of society.

Words rose to her lips, as eloquent as they were simple, and whispered silently, 'I love you, Clint.'

He did not hear but he drew away, to see the glancing tenderness in her eyes; that, and the glow of lips moist from his kisses seemed to drive him to madness and she was crushed again into the punishing strength of his arms, the male hardness of his virility stimulating every nerve fiber in her body until there was only the chaos of burning need of fulfillment, a need that was a wild, unbridled desire for the feel of his naked flesh against hers, his possessive hands seeking and taking, their pleasure her bliss; rapture and desire fulfilled.

But he drew away and as she looked into his eyes she saw all that her heart desired. He cared! Her body settled, but she was transported by her discovery to the heights of heaven, with earth a million light years away. The expression in his eyes was fulfillment as high and wide as eternity, setting her soul on fire.

She had been right when she said that true love was spiritual first, and physical next. She closed her eyes and lay contentedly against his chest.

'Stardust and dreams. . . .' Clint was murmuring. She felt the tenderness of his lips against her cheek, the reverent caress of his hand on her breast as if he were touching some precious object, almost sacred. 'Stardust and dreams, and true love is spiritual. . . .' He spoke to himself and she started up, feeling that in spirit he had left her.

'Clint. . . .' she whispered, bewilderment in her lovely eyes. 'You . . . ?' What was she trying to ask him? But he knew, surely. Suddenly she was afraid, and she whispered to herself, 'I need him! Oh, God, don't let him desert me!'

Suddenly his smile came, and he bent his head to kiss her tenderly on the mouth. All her world was rosy again, her fear dissolving like frost in the April sun. He cared; she had not been mistaken, and naturally her mind leaped to the deception she was practising but she saw no real problems. When the time came his "motherly" housekeeper would leave, having properly given in her notice, and would never be seen again. Or, should Clint want to be married soon, then Miss Waring would give in her notice earlier. It was simplicity itself.

'My dear, Karen,' Clint was saying softly. 'It's time I took you home.'

Home! The one small word brought her instantly back to reality, and to the fact that her position was now awkward, to say the least. When she had embarked upon this escapade the possibility of her falling in love with him had never entered her head. She had disliked Clint Fraser to the point of actual hatred, because of her resenting his unfair criticism of her acting.

'I want to—to get a taxi,' she murmured, drawing away from him and shaking her head. 'Please—'

'Nonsense, darling! Everything's changed. I must see you home.'

The dryness in her throat actually hurt as she tried to swallow. What could she do to extricate herself from this tangle? Clint's next words only made things worse, much worse. 'We've now to tell each other all about ourselves. I'll start first. I'm a playwright. And I'm on the boat because I wanted complete quiet, away from everyone—servants, friends and anyone else who might become a nuisance to me. That's why I advertised for Miss Waring, and why she has to leave the boat every day. Fortunately she had a sister here and that was an important factor when I was engaging her. It made things so much easier all round.' He stopped and because she was staring down at her feet he tilted her face with the masterful touch of a hand beneath her chin. 'And now, love, you can tell me about yourself. What are you doing here and where do you live? That will do for a start.'

She drew a deep breath, seeing her dreams come crashing about her ears. Should she confess all, throw herself on his mercy? He loved her and although he would undoubtedly be furious, he'd forgive her . . . or would he? She slanted him a glance in the moonlight, saw the inflexibility of his jaw, the firm chin and mouth, the unfathomable gray eyes that were now fixed upon her with fine-drawn intentness. No, she dared not make a confession! All would be lost if she did. Play for time, that was the thing to do, but how? Never in her life had she been in such a plight as she was at this moment. And then, out of the blue, an idea came which, although it might not work, was at least worth a try.

'It's so very late, Clint, and your housekeeper's on her own on the boat. I'd not like it if it were me. Women get nervous, you know.'

'But—'

'Men don't understand a woman's nervousness, Clint. Take me home another evening, when it's not so late, but for tonight—well, it's far more sensible for me to get a taxi.'

He was still frowning but as she watched the frown began to fade.

'Very well, but tomorrow, I want to know where you live and all about you. Understand?' Imperious were the words and the manner of their delivery.

Fairly sagging with relief, Karen offered the meek response, 'Yes, Clint, of course I understand.'

They walked hand in hand back to the hotel where Clint called two taxis and while they waited he asked her to meet him for dinner the following night.

'I shall be working hard all day,' he said with very noticeable satisfaction. 'I've been having trouble with the play I'm writing but I shall be able to carry on now—for a while at any rate. And by the way,' he added, smiling, 'I haven't told you my name. It's Fraser.'

'Fraser?' Karen looked suitably impressed, her eyes widening and a little exclamation escaping her. '*The* Clint Fraser, but it must be! There's only one.'

'Yes, dear,' he replied and as one of the taxis arrived at that moment he handed her into it and stood for a moment, tall and straight, incredibly attractive.

'Good night, until tomorrow,' she said, shining up at

him from her comfortable seat in the back of the car.

'Good night, dear—' He stooped to kiss her lips, an impulsive action, as if it were quite impossible to resist what Karen was unconsciously offering. 'Yes, until tomorrow; eight o'clock at the Southern Palms. I'll see you in the lobby.'

Chapter Seven

As was only to be expected, sleep would elude Karen that night; in her cabin she tossed and turned, desperate to discover a way out of the mess she had gotten herself into. Deceit never did pay; she had always known it. But this masquerade had never been considered as deliberate deceit; it had been so appealing to her at the time, and never in her wildest dreams could she have foreseen herself falling in love with the man she had so much disliked as to desire to be revenged on him. She had even given him a false name, and at the recollection she found herself weeping, as despair and hopelessness flooded over her. There was no way out; she would have to disappear—yes, Karen Boyle would have to disappear but not Miss Waring, for if his housekeeper disappeared Clint would immediately feel it his duty to go to the police. Yet how could she stay on as his housekeeper, loving him as she did?

A great shuddering sigh escaped her and she got up at last, switching on the light. A quarter past one and she had not yet slept a wink. She put on a thick velour dressing gown, wrapping it around her because she suddenly felt chilled to the bone. She would make a cup of tea she decided, and went silently to the galley. She had just brewed it and was about to pick it up from the table when to her horror she heard her employer moving about in the narrow space outside the door, which was, fortunately, closed.

'Miss Waring, are you all right?' The handle of the door was turning. There was a second's inaction as fear froze her limbs, then she was precipitated into motion, springing to the door and slamming it shut, even as he began to open it.

'Yes,' she cried breathlessly. 'Of—of c-course I'm all right.'

'I've been working and went on deck for a breath of fresh air. I saw the light and naturally wondered what was the matter. Are you sure you're all right?'

'Yes—yes! I've said so!' Thank God she'd remembered to use her assumed voice!

'Then why can't I come in?'

Wildly she glanced around, as if seeking inspiration from the stove or the sink or the cupboard where all the food was stored. And then, like a miracle, an idea came to her.

'I'm—er—in my night clothes, Mr. Fraser. . . .'

'Oh—sorry,' abruptly, and she sagged with relief as she heard his quiet measured tread as he walked along the passage.

Her heart was beating rapidly, pounding wildly

against her ribs. She looked at the tea, a restorative. Drawing her dressing gown more snugly around her she sat down at the table, too scared to make a move yet to go back to her cabin.

What must she do? Karen could not have counted the number of times this question had come to her since the moment Clint had said that they must now learn about one another. And the only answer was that she would have to make a full confession. Yet immediately upon this came the certainty that Clint would not understand her original motive and, therefore, he would be quite unable to forgive her.

If they had known each other a little longer, and their love had strengthened. . . .

Play for time. . . . This was the first idea that had come to her and she found herself dwelling on the possibility of doing just that. But how could she play for time? In, say, another few weeks, he would be so madly in love with her that, although he might be furious and deeply humiliated, she was sure he would never allow his pride to spoil both their lives. No, he could not—she was so convinced of it that she continued to dwell on the possibility of playing for time, and although no immediate way presented itself she felt much more relaxed and was able to sleep when presently she went cautiously from the galley to her cabin.

Clint was as usual in the dining saloon when she took in his breakfast the following morning. He looked at her but she pretended not to notice as she put down his glass of grapefruit juice and then the heated plate on which was the usual bacon and one egg.

He came forward unhurriedly and sat down at the table.

Karen was at the door when he said quietly, 'Miss Waring, whom did you send to do my shopping yesterday?'

'Who . . . ?' uncomprehendingly. 'I did it myself—' She stopped, her nerves springing to the alert.

'A lie is not necessary, Miss Waring,' he broke in censoriously. 'It doesn't matter to me who did the shopping so long as it was done. I was interested to know who it was, that was all. The chemist's a friend of mine and I happened to meet him before I dined last evening. I mentioned that I'd sent my housekeeper in yesterday for the items I required and he rather enviously asked me how I'd come to find such an exceptionally young and beautiful lady to be a housekeeper for me.'

Karen was trembling under his curious regard, but managed to pull herself together, her brain working furiously—and with success, much to her own surprise.

'Oh, it was the young lady who's staying in my sister's bungalow,' she returned, feeling sure her voice was hollow, and not at all like the one to which he was used. Unconsciously she was twisting her fingers; she saw him looking at them and her acting ability was brought into service. 'I'm very sorry, Mr. Fraser. I feel guilty at not doing it myself. After all, my duties are very light. But Helen was going into Bridgetown and she offered, so—' She broke off, shrugging apologetically, her heart as heavy as lead because of all the deceit she was having to practise. She felt weighed down with the ineffable burden of it and for one impulsive moment she could have thrown off her wig and spectacles, and revealed who she was.

But the impulse was controlled, and in any case, he was speaking again, 'So you're not on your own all day as I surmised? I've been a little troubled about you since your sister went away. Is this young lady staying long?'

'She came for three weeks; she still has a fortnight to go.'

'She's here on her own?' He seemed puzzled and Karen explained that the arrangements were made for the holiday before her sister went away.

'I see,' he toyed with the stem of his glass, a thoughtful expression on his face. 'She must have been disappointed.' Karen said nothing and after a pause Clint asked unexpectedly, 'Would you like to sleep at the bungalow, Miss Waring?'

'Sleep?'

'I feel I might be dining out rather more often in the future, at least for a while. And it will leave you free in the evenings. So you could stay with your sister's friend. It would be nicer for you both, wouldn't it?'

'Yes, it certainly would.'

'That's what I thought. It isn't very nice for you to be coming here in the dark anyway, nor is it necessary. So you can stay at the bungalow by all means. As long as you serve my breakfast at eight in the morning, and do your other jobs, then you can take the rest of the days and evenings off.'

'It's very good of you,' she murmured. 'Helen will be very happy to have me sleeping at the bungalow at night.'

'Yes, I'm sure she will.' He picked up his glass of fruit juice. 'So that's settled, then.'

After rushing round Clint's suite and then making his sandwiches, Karen was quite naturally unable to settle to any of the normal chores, so she merely cleared away Clint's breakfast dishes and was soon leaving the boat. She hurried along the beach to where she could enter the grounds of the Smuggler's Cove Hotel and from there to her sister's bungalow.

'You're early!' exclaimed Helen, who was tidying up the living room. 'You make me more envious every day.'

Karen sat down, something she never did until she had rid herself of her disguise.

'Well, you'll not be envious of me in a few minutes.' She looked at Helen through shadowed eyes. 'I'm in a terrible mess.'

Helen whistled, expelling a breath.

'He's guessed and you've gotten the sack. . . .' Her voice trailed to silence as Karen shook her head.

'No, he hasn't guessed. My job's safe enough. It isn't that at all.' Her lip trembled but she pulled herself together. It was all her own fault and self-pity was not only out of place but futile.

'What is it, then?'

Karen hesitated, then said she would get out of her disguise and tell her all about it.

Automatically Helen followed her to the bedroom, to stand at the door, watching her almost tear off the dress, and apply pads of makeup remover to her face.

'You've not fallen in love with the man?' she queried narrowly.

'Yes,' choked Karen, 'I have.'

'Lord—what a fine kettle of fish, and no mistake! I ought to find it amusing and yet—'

'Please don't laugh,' begged Karen, going over to the washbasin and turning on the tap. 'I couldn't bear it.'

'I'll make some coffee,' was Helen's practical decision and she disappeared, a troubled expression on her face.

A quarter of an hour later, having gone out into the sunlight of the patio to drink their coffee, Karen was pouring out the whole wretched story, omitting only the scene enacted on the beach.

'My only hope is to play for time,' she ended, looking at her friend for inspiration.

'What a mess! Who'd have thought that a situation like this could possibly have occurred? It seemed such an exciting, enviable adventure when you told me about it that night at the hotel. I don't know what to advise. . . .' She tailed off thoughtfully. 'You really want to play for time? You wouldn't chance telling him everything?'

'Would you, if you were in my position?'

'No,' replied Helen instantly, 'I would not. As you've said, he hasn't known you long enough.' She stopped, pursing her lips. 'It's remarkable that he's fallen for you. It's different with you; you know who he is, and all about him. You know he's an honourable man—

well, he's looked up to and well-known. But he knows absolutely nothing about you—not even your age, your occupation or where you live—nothing! It's incredible that a man like that would fall in love under such circumstances, and so quickly. I should have thought he'd have been more cautious.' Helen's glance was troubled, her forehead creased in a frown. 'Are you quite sure that he's in love with you?'

Karen swallowed convulsively.

'Quite sure, Helen,' she nodded. 'He's not the kind of man to pretend. I just know instinctively that he isn't pretending. Besides, what good would it do for him to pretend?'

'None that I can see,' conceded Helen, but a small sigh escaped her. However, after a while she said more briskly, 'Well, Karen, if you're determined to have him, and as you can't afford to take any chances, let us get our heads together and try to sort it out. You've mentioned that he's willing for you to stay here every night after you've served him his dinner, and that certainly makes things easier because you haven't to go back to the boat. But the difficult thing is that you can't let him take you home—'

'And he wants to take me home *tonight*,' interrupted Karen almost in tears. 'I can't let him—and yet if I don't he's bound to be suspicious. I can't keep on putting him off, not now that we're in love—' Her voice cut abruptly as Helen suddenly snapped her fingers, her blue eyes lighting up.

'I have it,' Helen cried triumphantly. 'And it not only solves one problem but two at least! The apartment—it's standing empty. You're on holiday, staying there for three weeks— Well, for another fortnight. How's that? It takes care of where you're staying, and the reason for your being on the island.' She looked at Karen who was too dumbfounded to speak. 'Well, is it a good idea or isn't it?' demanded Helen, a trifle deflated by her friend's silence.

'It's a marvelous idea!' agreed Karen. 'Helen, you're a genius! Why on earth didn't I think of that? I couldn't sleep last night and had to get up and make a cup of tea.' She thought of telling Helen about the incident of Clint's coming to the galley but changed her mind, there being more pressing matters to discuss at the moment. 'A fortnight,' she murmured. 'That'll not be long enough.'

'It gives you breathing space.'

'Yes, indeed.' Karen became thoughtful, her spirits having lifted so that clear thinking was again possible. 'I could probably rent the apartment for a longer period, seeing that it's the off-season here at present.'

'But if you're on holiday,' began Helen, when Karen interrupted her.

'I'm going to tell Clint I've thrown up my job, and tell him why.'

'That'll give you a good reason for prolonging your stay—which Clint will want you to do, of course. How long do you think he'll be before he proposes?'

'I don't know. It's all happened so suddenly.'

'Too suddenly for my liking,' Helen felt impelled to say. 'Are you quite sure he's genuine? You've mentioned this other girl—and admit he said it could be serious. Is he intending to throw her over?'

Karen frowned, thinking of that fleeting moment last night when Clint had seemed so far away, bringing an access of fear to her heart.

'Don't make me doubt him, Helen,' she pleaded.

Helen's lashes flickered down, hiding her expression. Yet she just had to say, 'You're not quite sure, are you, Karen—? No, don't interrupt because what I'm going to say is logical. If you *were* sure—a hundred percent sure—then you'd not hesitate to go to him and open up.'

Karen's lips were suddenly dry, because what Helen said was true.

She thrust her doubts away; they were too unbearable to harbor, for if she lost Clint now she felt she would never get over it.

'He *will* propose,' she stated emphatically, 'I know it! But although we'll be engaged, I feel he'll not want to be married until his play's finished. Marriage would be too much of an upheaval.'

'And in the meantime Miss Waring is to continue in her post of housekeeper?'

'Of course. There's no reason for her—me—to leave. Clint would be in a mess without someone to get his breakfast and do the chores.'

'You'll be seeing him regularly?'

'Yes. He told me this morning that he wouldn't want me to cook his main meals as often as in the past—at least for a while, so he's obviously intending to see me every night.'

'For a while?' repeated Helen, suddenly suspicious. 'Why the qualification?'

'I can't say. It isn't important.'

'You're sure?'

'Helen, please believe that he's genuine. I know he is!'

'All right, forget it. He'll be seeing you home every

time you go out, so you and I had better go along to the apartment today and take a few things that'll make it look lived in. There are only the bare bones there at present as you know. You mustn't forget the key, either, when you go out. I've put it in the top drawer in Jean's dressing table.' She paused but Karen made no comment. 'You'll come back here every night, after he's left you?'

'Yes, I shall have to because of my disguise. It takes some time as you know, and I've got to be on the boat by seven at the latest. I'll have to be up at half-past six. I hope I shan't disturb you.'

'Not at all; I'm up at that time. The sun's pouring into my window so it would be impossible to sleep even if I wanted to, which I don't. The early mornings here are too wonderful.' Helen was silent for a while and then, 'You're seeing him tonight?'

'I hoped you wouldn't mind?'

'Not in the least. As a matter of fact, I can go dancing with a bloke from the hotel here. I met him yesterday morning just before you arrived. He's on his own and gave me his room number, telling me to phone him if I cared to go dancing with him.'

Clint was already at the hotel when Karen arrived by taxi, looking adorably young and unsophisticated in an ankle length dress of cornflower blue whose perfect cut accentuated her delicate curves and the boyish slimness of her waist. Her hair, cloud-like about her shoulders, the play of light on her tanned skin, the liquid beauty of her eyes . . . all these were taken in by the man who, tall, assured, and with a sort of dynamic grace in his movements, was coming toward her, a smile softening the stern reserve of his features. Envious eyes were turned upon Karen from every woman in the lobby; a tentative rapture stole through her nerves and her heart was light with joy. Clint's polished manners were portrayed in the slight inclination of his head in greeting, and in the way he put his hand beneath her elbow, a gesture of gallantry, and a winning smile was his instant reward. He ushered her away toward a winding staircase leading to a balcony overlooking the gardens and the drowsy Caribbean. As always it was a magical scene, with a million stars in the dark sapphire sky and the moon filtering wraith-like clouds to embroider the landscape with fragile patterns of delicate fretwork. Karen, a sigh of contentment on her lips, leaned back in the chair which Clint had drawn out for her. He studied her from his place opposite, seeming to be taking in every change in her features resulting from the gentle play of light created by the movement of foliage against the lamps which had been placed within it. Only one other couple was on the balcony, seated right at the far end, and it seemed to Karen, glancing over gardens drenched in moonlight to the palm-fringed shore beyond, that she and Clint had the entire world to themselves. She was on air, so happy that she was frightened.

'What are you thinking?' Clint teetered back in his chair as if wishing to view the lovely picture from a greater distance. But his manner faintly disconcerted her, and she now realised that even as she had entered the lobby she had sensed there was something different about him. 'Your face tells me you're happy and yet I sense anxiety. You can confide, you know, dear. I shall be more than interested to listen.'

Her eyes flew to his, nerves springing to the alert at his keen perception.

'Why should I be anxious?' she asked, unable to find anything else to say.

'There could be many reasons,' was his cryptic reply and now her eyes fell before the keen examination of his. 'However, tell me about yourself. Where do you live on this island and why are you here?' he went on when she did not speak.

She told him she was on holiday, and that she was in an apartment on the grounds of the Coral Court Hotel.

'On holiday? On your own?'

'Yes.'

'You had no friend who would come with you?' That disconcerting quality in his manner was still there and a prickling sensation ran the length of Karen's spine. Some sixth sense warned her that this ought to be the moment of truth, and for one impulsive second she toyed with the idea of speaking out, of ending the anxiety he had spoken of. Anxiety? It was so much more than that! But she cast the idea aside. What was between her and Clint was too slender a foundation to support the truth at this stage. No, she must wait . . . and hope.

'I wanted to come alone,' she replied eventually. 'One does need to be alone at times.'

He nodded in agreement, bringing his chair back to the table as the waiter appeared, ready to take the order for their drinks. Karen watched him give the order, noting the chiseled leanness of his bronzed face, his air of culture and good taste, the aura of male confidence about him, accentuated by the languid tone he used. And yet he was gracious as he smilingly requested the waiter to bring two menus with the drinks.

'How long are you here for?' he asked when the waiter had gone.

'Three weeks, initially, but I've already had one.' She had seen about retaining the apartment earlier in the day and had been told that she could have it indefinitely.

'Initially?'

'I can stay longer if I wish.'

'You have employment in—' he stopped as if he had made a slip '—at home?'

'I gave up my job just before I came here. I worked in an office and when my boss retired I was to be transferred to a man I detested. So I decided to leave, intending to get another post on my return.' That at least was the truth, even if it was subtly manipulated, thought Karen, but she did wonder how many more lies would be told before the final confession was made.

'That was rather drastic, wasn't it?' He was frowning, as if he considered her to have been recklessly unwise.

So he was not contemplating marriage yet. It was as she had surmised: he intended finishing his play first.

'I didn't think so at the time. I could never have worked for the other man.'

'Where is your home?' The question came after a slight hesitation, and Clint was staring beyond her as he spoke.

'London. I have a flat there.'

'You live alone?'

She nodded; her hair swayed, catching the light which brought out the enchanting tints of tawny-gold.

'Yes, I live alone.'

'You've no parents?'

'They were killed in a train accident four years ago.'

Clint's face softened to compassion.

'That must have been terrible for you. How old were you at the time?'

'Eighteen.'

'So you're twenty-two now.' He paused a moment, becoming thoughtful. 'Have you other relatives?'

'I've a sister.' Now, she thought somberly, was when the lies would have to begin.

Clint was looking puzzled.

'If you've only one relative—this sister—why don't you live together—' He broke off, smiling ruefully. 'It's not your sister I want to learn about, but you. Just sit there Karen and talk about yourself.' His voice seemed to have undergone a slight change—nothing tangible and yet a strange uneasiness assailed her. For a while she was relieved that he did not want her to talk about her sister—since to do so would mean she would have to lie—at the same time Karen considered it very strange indeed that he should be so casual about the girl who would eventually become his sister-in-law. Clint was speaking again, and there was an unfathomable expression in his eyes as he added, 'What do you do with your leisure time? Tell me about your hobbies.'

Her long dark lashes fluttered down. Now was the time for subtleties, for avoidance, where possible, of deliberate lies. He had asked about her hobbies and obviously the information to leave out was that she belonged to an amateur dramatic society.

She began to talk—about her childhood which was happy, about the time when at eighteen, she and her sister, younger by two years, had been left to fend for themselves.

'The house was ours, of course,' she went on, 'but there was not very much money. And so we both left school and found work. Later, when my sister obtained a post abroad we decided to sell the house and share the money. I put the deposit down on a flat and that took most of my money because flats in London are so expensive, and the house we sold was neither large nor in a very good state of repair.' She had been looking at him, but now her eyes wandered, thrusts of scarlet hibiscus and purple bougainvillea catching her immediate attention as floodlights were switched on to illuminate the terrace down below where the steel band was assembling at one end.

During the whole of her narrative Clint had been listening with unmoving countenance, as if he were waiting for one particular piece of information. And when finally she said, 'And that's all. Mine hasn't been a very exciting life,' there was an impenetrable expression on his face and an odd inflection in his voice as he said, 'Your hobbies—' Clint's eyes were sharp, uncomfortably searching. 'You haven't mentioned them.'

'My hobbies?' she repeated, having difficulty in keeping her voice steady, for she had caught the measured significance in the content of his words. 'I love reading—biographies and poetry mainly—' She paused, the sensation of impalpable feathers touching her spine. 'I swim and play tennis, and recently I've tried my hand at painting.'

Silence. Etched into the now austere male features was an expression of deep censure.

'Karen,' he murmured very softly at last, 'I did say, a few minutes ago, that you could confide—that I would listen with interest.'

He knew of her deception! For a paralysed second it seemed that her heart had stopped beating. Yes, he knew . . . but where was the fury she had expected. True, he was regarding her sternly, and by some trick of the light his face was more formidable than ever before. But no sign of anger was portrayed. If he *had* learned of the masquerade surely she would not be here now, drinking cocktails on this flower-bedecked balcony with the moon-flushed gardens below and the soft West Indian music drifting up to them!

Still fearful, her limpid eyes bewilderedly enlarged, she asked in a low tone, 'Clint . . . why are you—you talking t-to me like this?'

'I believe you know,' he replied and although the sternness came through, not a trace of anger affected the even tenor of his voice.

Karen could only stare, the hand holding her glass shaking slightly, because of the wild beating of her heart.

'You've somehow learned of the deception?' Even as the words were out she regretted them. He could *not* know! For the strength of anger resulting from the knowledge that he'd been duped, made a complete fool of, could never be repressed to this extent.

'Your chief hobby's acting. You belong to the Parkside Amateur Dramatic Society. You were in my play, *One Stolen Hour*—'

'Oh, Clint!' she cried, unable to keep from breaking in. 'Why aren't you angry? How can you be so calm about a deception of such magnitude?' Her eyes were moist, her face as white as the coat of the waiter who had come to take their order for dinner. 'Why . . . ?' Her tremulous voice faded to a questioning silence as she saw the perplexity in his eyes.

'Good heavens, Karen,' he said reassuringly, 'it isn't all that serious. Magnitude?' He smiled indulgently. 'It's only a minor deception which hasn't done any harm at all.'

'No . . . harm?' She blinked at him dazedly. 'No harm to—to us? To your opinion of me? But it must have!' she cried without giving him the opportunity to answer. 'For me to adopt the disguise of—'

'Disguise?' he echoed, looking at her as if she were a little unhinged. 'Karen, my silly child, I'm staggered that you could consider you'd committed a crime. I can fully understand why you didn't enlighten me that you were Gloria Standish in my play, because I seem to remember that I wasn't particularly nice to you on the occasion we have in mind. And afterwards, on the hotel grounds, I fear you might have heard my totally unwarranted remark about your acting ability. It was unforgivable of me and I now revise my opinion. I have to,' he continued wryly, 'because about a quarter of an hour before you arrived I was on the terrace and a man came up to me. He'd recognised me as Clint Fraser, and said he wanted me to know just how well the Parkside Amateur Dramatic Society had performed my play, *One Stolen Hour*. He and his wife are regular supporters of the company. They had seen the play and considered the acting excellent. He saw me with you last evening but did not want to intrude. If I was seeing the young lady again would I convey the message that she was superb in her role of Gloria Standish and he and his wife hoped to see her again when the next season begins. Don't look so tragic,' he teased. 'There's no harm done.'

She managed a smile, but her heart was still heavy. He knew only a minor part. That was the reason for his lack of anger; and it was no wonder he considered her to be attaching too much importance to the matter.

'I'm sorry about what I said regarding your acting, Karen,' he said contritely. 'I realised afterward that I was wrong and in fact I came to find you and apologise, and to take it all back but you'd gone home.' He smiled and, leaning forward, he covered her hand with his. 'It's understandable that you'd be reluctant to tell me you were the bitch in my play whose acting I'd criticised. I don't blame you, but tonight, I wanted you to confess, and that's why I asked you to talk about your hobbies.' His fingers tightened around her hand. She thrilled to the warmth and tenderness of his touch but a weight still lay on her spirits. If only he had guessed *all* and taken it so calmly. . . . But of course that was impossible. If he *had* guessed all he could never have remained so calm about it. However, there was only one deception now—the major one, but at least he now knew who she was, the girl in the play.

'I suppose I ought to have told you,' she admitted.

'It was natural that you'd not want me to know—' He broke off, eyeing her quizzically. 'I'd have had to know sometime, darling,' he told her and those words wiped away all her dejection and a lovely smile lit her face.

'Thank you for not being angry with me, Clint,' she murmured, but he interrupted her to say, 'Am I forgiven?'

She choked on the words as she said,

'*I* have nothing to forgive, Clint—oh, nothing at all!'

The taxi drew away and Karen inserted the key in the door of the apartment where she was supposed to be living. Her heart was beating rapidly because Clint had insisted that he come inside to say goodnight, and she knew a delicate and exciting access of expectancy as she turned to him after he had closed the door behind her.

'This is the living room,' she flicked a hand expressively.

'Very comfortable. Almost as good as my boat.'

'Oh, not as good as your boat—' she began, then stopped, nerves quivering at the slip. 'I mean—well, they were talking about your boat at the party, and I gathered it was something rather special.'

He nodded his head.

'*I* think it is. You must come over soon and I'll show it to you.' He had come close, a towering giant whose features were carved in masculine perfection. With a little cry of pleasure she went gladly into his inviting arms, feeling small and helpless, utterly compliant beneath his strong male dominance.

After-shave still lingered—the scent of pines and heather moors and the freshness of dawn all mingling to drug her senses to a profound awareness of the male appeal of him. The vital force of sexual desire controlled her mind; rapture caught her throat at the closeness of his virile body as his arms brought her possessively against him. His kiss sent blood pulsing through her veins, driven by the rising turbulence of her emotions. Her lips parted to his masterful command and his tongue explored the sweetness of her mouth. She was so close that she could feel the sinewed hardness of thighs, the muscular strength of his loins as he thrust them against her slender frame. A sigh that was a whisper of sheer ecstasy escaped before her lips were crushed again as his moistly sensuous mouth enclosed hers, the roughness of his tongue sending fire through her veins. Her whole body quivered within his embrace as she soared to ecstatic heights of bliss when his hand strayed possessively to the tender curve of a breast and the rising nipple hardened to the pleasure-pain of his insistent fingers. Her body was no longer her own for the natural instinct of male dominance was strong within her, and surrender to this dominance was her own fulfillment. Yet in her surrender there was no subservience. Subconsciously she conveyed this to him. Her capitulation was honourable, of his persuasion but *her* choosing. Her own power was equal to his, though not manifest; her gifts were bestowed freely—not the spoil of a conqueror flaunting his power. Her love was a tender, sacred offering and she gladly gave when he wanted to take, arching her seductive frame in response to the stormy torment of the possessive hand that crept to the lower part of her body, sensuously caressing her soft flesh while at the same time compelling her to come closer to the thrusting male hardness of his loins.

'You intoxicate me.' His voice was frayed by passion, his breath hot against her face, his hands warm and strong as he lifted her. Carrying her to the divan he laid her down, a smile of tenderness curving his mouth as he stood for a long moment, his eyes devouring the beauty of her body, the alluring rise and fall of her breasts, the tempting feminine contours which the dress outlined in tantalising allure. He lay down beside her, a hand cupping her small firm breast within its lean brown strength. Ecstasy vibrated through her limbs; her arms came about him and she turned her body into his, her hand gently tugging at his shirt, bringing it out so that she could feel the leanness of the flesh covering his ribs.

'Karen . . . my own darling! I can't wait for you! You'll come to me?' He held her from him, his eyes dark with latent passion and virility, and in hers the dreamy cloud of longing. 'I want you now—this moment.'

The merest hesitation, and then, 'Yes, darling. . . .' Her voice was a warm temptation, and for long, long moments his passion flared and Karen was swept headlong into its turbulence as his body heaved above her, thrusting its hardness against her loins. 'Let me take your dress off. . . .' His hands manipulated the fastener, sliding it down.

Karen never afterward knew just how and when she changed her mind. It seemed all wrong, somehow, to make love like this, sullying what ought to be pure and sweet and undefiled. She whispered, holding his hand against her cheek, 'I don't want it to be this way, Clint.' It was a cry from the depths of a body chaste and clean. 'Please let us wait.'

For an instant it seemed that he had traveled too far along the path of desire to draw back, but the expression in her eyes, the plea in a voice that trembled childishly, were too much for his honour and he came away.

'How right you are, my love. . . .' With gentle fingers he zipped up her dress again, then drew her to him, to kiss her tenderly on the lips. 'I'm so very glad you changed your mind. It was important that you should.'

'Important?' She looked at him, her eyes still dark and drowsy from his lovemaking. 'Important,' she repeated, her heart skipping a beat for what appeared to be no reason at all.

'Yes, but I can't explain.' Releasing her, he moved away and tucked his shirt back into his slacks. He brought out a comb, pushing it through his thick shining hair, and as she watched he seemed, as on several previous occasions, to be making mental notes. The wraith of an idea filtered into her consciousness only to be instantly thrust away.

He was *not* using her as "copy" for his play! He wouldn't do a thing like that to her!

Chapter Eight

They stood outside the door of the apartment, holding hands, trying to say good night but the minutes stretched and still Clint made no move to go.

The gardens around them were illuminated by lights in the trees and bushes; the moon, argent and cold, sailed along between cloud banks, lending a strange aura of mystery to the scene. The trade wind blew gently, swaying the trees to create shadows that were pitched, swooping like night birds seeking prey. The sea, drowsy and smooth, spread away to be lost in a mist of opal light.

'Well, Karen, I really must make a move. It's past midnight and you ought to be in bed.' Taking her in his arms Clint bent his head and kissed her softly parted lips. 'I shan't—' He hesitated as if reluctant to voice what was in his mind. And it was with mixed feelings that Karen heard him say, 'As I want the play finished in as little time as possible I shan't be seeing you for a few days, but I'll be thinking about you.'

So he wanted it finished as soon as possible! Her heart leaped with joy.

The sacrifice was worth it because the sooner he finished the play the sooner they would be married.

'I understand,' she smiled.

'I know now where you are so I can easily get in touch.'

'I'm out for most of the time,' she returned, once again aware of some slight misgiving. Why wasn't he making a definite date?

'I'll leave a note—or, better still, I can phone the hotel. They'll give you the message. Good night, Karen. Sleep well.'

She stood watching his long strides taking him toward the hotel, where he would be able to get a taxi. Only when he was lost to view in the mothy darkness of the shrubbery did she turn and enter the apartment. She felt flat, drained in a way that frightened her. Helen had been very skeptical about Clint's sincerity, and Helen had always been very astute. . . .

The idea that he was using her persisted, strengthened by certain things recalled, unbidden, by her mind. Clint had said his heroine was unsatisfactory as he had had her; he wanted her to be both unusual and unpredictable . . . and that was how he had described *her*—right at the very beginning. He had wanted to know more about her, he said. Another point was that after he had been out with her he was able to tell his housekeeper that his heroine was now satisfactory. This had happened twice . . . and each time it was after he had been with her, dining and dancing . . . and making love.

'He *can't* have been using me! Oh, I just *know* he's

genuine!' But the wish was father to the thought; she had to admit it because of the unsettling qualms which she was unable to shake off.

She went to the hotel and got a taxi; ten minutes later she was entering the bungalow to find that Helen had just a moment ago come in.

'Hello! And how is the romance progressing? I think I'm in the same boat—I rather like my new boy friend. . . .' Helen's voice faded on a note of anxiety as she saw Karen's expression. 'It's finished?'

'No—well, I can't say.' Karen was close to tears but determinedly she held them back. 'He's using me—' Breaking off she shook her head. 'I can't believe he'd be so hateful, so specious!' She looked at Helen through stricken eyes. 'He just isn't that kind of man.'

'What kind of man?' inquired Helen patiently.

'I had an idea—it came to me when we were in the apartment.' She stopped, still reluctant to say what was on her mind.

'Yes? You had an idea?'

Karen moistened her lips.

'Helen, do you think he could be using me as copy for his play?'

'Using you?' Helen's blue eyes widened. 'No—I mean, the thought never occurred to me. What was the reason it occurred to you?'

Karen gave her a full explanation and when she had finished Helen's eyes were deeply troubled.

'I hate to say it, Karen, but it certainly does seem that your idea was correct.'

'What a fool I am,' quivered Karen bitterly. 'It's Clint who's been doing the acting. I think I hate him.'

'I'm very sure you do not,' declared Helen. 'However, that's unimportant. What is important is that although things look black against him, we ought not to jump to conclusions at this stage.'

'How am I to find out, one way or another?'

'It's simplicity itself. You have access to his study. All you must do is take a look at some of the pages of his manuscript.'

'Of course! I've never looked yet; I felt it would be wrong—prying, sort of.'

'Well, you'll have to take a look now, just to put your mind at rest.'

At rest. . . . If she discovered he'd been deceiving her she felt that her mind would never be at rest again.

As soon as she had taken in Clint's breakfast the following morning Karen went along to his study as usual but this time her first act was to go over to a table and look at some of the papers lying there. They gave her no clue but as there was little time she decided to look at the manuscript itself, which was always on the desk; Karen had watched it grow, marveling at Clint's ability to write so much in a day. It was upside down; she turned it over to look at the beginning and saw the title at the top of the page! *Stardust and Dreams*. And it had been typed in at a different time from the first page, as the letters were less black.

With pulsating nerves she turned the manuscript over again to leaf through some of the last pages, and it needed only a brief examination to confirm her suspicions; Clint *had* been using her, acting a part so that he could discover her reaction, which was the copy he required. She stood for a moment, her eyes dark with pain for, strangely it wasn't a shock, but a drained, sickening feeling in the pit of her stomach. She put the papers back, unwilling to search for those parts that might refer to the intimate side of their association—although she had the strong conviction that he would not put anything like that in the play, simply because he had never done so before, at least, not to her knowledge. She had seen two of his plays on television and one in a London theatre and in none had there been any intimate scenes such as had been enacted between Clint and herself.

Quickly she began to vacuum the carpet, but she had not finished when Clint entered, to stand for a moment in surprise.

'It's taken you a little longer this morning?'

'Yes—sorry.' Forcing a smile as a barrier to the almost irrepressible urge to tell him who she was and that she knew of his deceit, she added, 'I shan't be more than five minutes, but if you'd prefer that I leave it—?'

'No; carry on. I can wait. Oh, and by the way, I've had a change of plans. I'll be dining on the boat for the next few evenings.' He went off and had not returned when Karen went back to the dining saloon to clear away his breakfast dishes. Her mind was working to full capacity, with revenge rising above her heartache. She was level headed enough to realise that a man like that was not worth having and, therefore, she had lost nothing. She was determined to view her situation objectively, remembering that she was not the first girl to suffer disillusionment at the hands of a man.

But she had no intention of letting him get away with it; she would give him copy—of a kind he would certainly be happy to have!

Helen was very quiet after having been told that Clint definitely had been using Karen for his own ends, making up to her, pretending to be in love with her just to collect copy for his play.

'It's a wonder you didn't grasp the fact that he wasn't genuine,' said Helen frowningly at last.

'I agree, especially as he never actually said he loved me.'

Helen's eyes opened wide.

'He didn't?'

Karen shook her head.

'No, but he acted as if he did and I just took it for granted. I expect it's inexperience—but it'll never happen again!'

'Pity you had to learn the hard way,' said Helen sympathetically.

'I'm glad you were here, Helen. I'd feel even more unhappy if I'd been on my own.' It struck her that Helen had come for a holiday, and she made a firm resolve not to dwell on her own misfortune but to try to put on a false front, just for her friend's sake. And so she said casually, 'I'm not going to fret over it. I'm not the first girl who's been duped—' She stopped, colour fluctuating in her cheeks. 'I suppose you could say I've only got my deserts—for the deception *I* have been practising.'

'No, it's not the same at all; there was no real malice in what you were doing, no intent to hurt.' She paused, then asked the obvious question. 'What about Miss Waring?'

'I've decided to give him a week's notice and leave.'

'Good for you! It'll do him good to have to cook his own meals!'

'It's only his breakfast and dinner—and not always his dinner as you know. I expect he'll get someone else anyway.'

'You'll give in your notice tomorrow?'

Karen nodded.

'Yes, first thing,' she replied tightly, the pain in her heart excruciating in spite of her resolve, and the fact that she had sensibly accepted that Clint was not worth having anyway.

'You could settle for the showdown,' suggested Helen. 'At least it would give you the satisfaction of confounding him.'

'I've thought of it but I want to meet him again. He says he might phone the Coral Court Hotel or slip a note under the door of the apartment.'

'You want to see him?' Helen looked at her, puzzled.

'Yes. If it's copy he's after then he'll get it—but not the kind he wants!'

Helen's eyes flickered perceptively.

'I don't know quite how you're going to go about it but I'm glad you're fighting back.'

'What about you?' queried Karen, as the thought suddenly struck her. 'Last night you were saying something about your new boy friend.'

'Roger—yes.' Helen's blue eyes were alight. 'We got on like a house on fire. Kindred spirits—you know, the kind you just sense is your sort of person.'

'Yes . . . I know.' Karen successfully hid her own

fierce, jarring pain as she said, 'How long is he here for?'

'He works at the hotel; he's in the office. That's why he has the evenings off.' She paused, biting her lip. 'I've said I'll see him every night, but I don't like leaving you—'

'I'll be all right,' interrupted Karen reassuringly. And then she added, 'If it develops what will you do? He's English, I suppose?'

'Yes, from Brighton originally, but like Jean he wanted to get a job abroad. He came here on holiday but with the intention of trying for a job in one of the hotels, and he was lucky, getting in the office rather than being a waiter or barman, because then he'd have had to work in the evenings. You asked what I'll do if it develops. Well, I'd like to get a job here too, but, meanwhile, I shall have to go home as planned, then come back later.'

'I'll be coming home with you,' Karen said. 'But I too might come back and try for a job. I'd like to be closer to Jean, but I'll not come back until Clint's gone.'

Helen made no comment on this, but suggested they go into Bridgetown and look around the shops. Karen agreed and it was when they were in a restaurant having lunch that, through an arch which led to another large dining room, Karen espied Clint . . . and his companion was the girl he had been with at Sam Lord's Castle. So he wasn't working after all. He was out enjoying himself with the girl he would probably marry.

'Anything wrong?' from Helen on noticing the sudden pallor of her friend's face.

Karen shook her head instantly. She was not going

to spoil Helen's lunch by telling her that Clint was in there with another girl.

'Nothing. This lobster's delicious, isn't it?'

'Lovely. As I've said more than once, I shan't get used to my beans on toast in a hurry.'

Karen smiled but made no comment. It was only natural that despite her resolve she should keep thinking of Clint, especially when he was so close, lunching with another girl. She glimpsed him now and then but he was far too engrossed with his companion even to glance up. Well, the idea of giving him her notice was at least satisfying, and she was very glad, the following morning, to see the consternation on his face when she told him she would be leaving his employ.

'You're giving me a week's notice?' Clint stared at her disbelievingly. 'But you knew, Miss Waring, when you accepted the post, that it was for six months.'

She nodded, swallowing the hurtful little lump in her throat. How she loved him! It was so hard to leave him, knowing he needed her, and yet she was determined to harden her heart, to keep in her mind what he had done to her. He was not deserving of the least consideration, and she was firmly resolved that he would not get it.

'I didn't know just what it would be like, Mr. Fraser. I'm not cut out for life on a boat.'

'Your life isn't spent on the boat,' he reminded her sharply.

'It isn't the sort of post I expected,' she returned, adopting a stubborn attitude. 'I'm leaving, Mr. Fraser; I've made up my mind so there isn't anything you can say that would make me change it.'

'Not if I offer you more money?'

'I'm overpaid as it is.'

'This is very sudden, Miss Waring?' His gray eyes were narrowed and searching.

'I agree—but I want to leave.'

'You do realise that you are letting me down badly?'

'I have to think of myself,' she said shortly.

'You've another post in view? Is that it?'

Karen shook her head.

'Your breakfast's getting cold.' Her eyes slid to the heated plate on the table. 'I shall be leaving a week from today.'

'Just a moment—don't go, Miss Waring. You haven't offered me any kind of explanation, so I'm at a complete loss as to why you've suddenly sprung this on me. I consider you have no justification for your attitude in refusing to give me an explanation.'

She was hot beneath her greasepaint but she managed to sound cool and casual as she said, sidestepping the comments he had just made, 'There's no argument, Mr. Fraser, so please don't let's waste words. I'm determined to leave next Monday. That gives you time to get someone else.'

His scrutiny was keen, interrogating; naturally he was nonplused, because for one thing she had never spoken to him so sharply; her voice had always been edged with respect.

'So you're not willing to give me the explanation which I'm entitled to?' Anger was linked to the perplexity in his voice. 'Well, if that's what you want—' A flip of his hand denoted his disgust, and his unwillingness to carry the conversation further. 'You may go, Miss Waring.' He reached for his grapefruit, his manner one of icy impassivity. She stumbled blindly from the saloon, tears ruining the heavy makeup on her face. She removed it in her cabin and then, stealthily, left the boat and made her way to the bungalow.

Karen went to the apartment each day, in case there was a note under the door, or any messages for her at the hotel. It was not until the third day after she had given in her notice that she found a note had been slipped beneath the door. With trembling hands she slit the envelope.

'Will you dine with me tonight? I'll call for you at half-past seven. Love, Clint.'

Love. . . . Karen set her teeth as anger flowed through her, fiery in its intensity. It was obvious that he was running short of copy and so he was dating her in order to collect more. She glanced to the top of the page to see the date. Yes, she would dine with him tonight. And yes, she would give him the opportunity of collecting copy!

She was waiting when he arrived, and in spite of herself she was still seeing in him all that was perfect—the even white teeth when he smiled, the firm yet sensuous mouth, the long lithe body giving the impression of latent virility.

'Well, my love, I see you're ready.' He made to take her in his arms but she dodged away, saying,

'Not now, Clint. You'll spoil my lip rouge.'

'You can repair it,' he laughed, advancing towards her, grace and confidence in every step he took. He was in white slacks and a pale blue jacket, fashioned in the draped line, popular in warm countries for casual elegance and comfort. He took her hand, pulling her to him. 'What's wrong with you?' he asked, sudden anxiety in his voice. 'Aren't you feeling good?'

How well he did it she thought, pretending to be concerned when all he wanted was to use her, because he had come to a standstill again.

She let him kiss her, resolutely holding her emotions in check.

'You don't need to repair anything,' he said on releasing her. 'Come on, dear, I've a taxi outside. We're going to the Sugar Cane Club. There's a good show on tonight.'

The hotel was packed but Clint had booked a table with a good view of the small stage where the steel band was playing. In the taxi he had told her that his housekeeper was leaving but there was a lack of real concern in his manner. Obviously he had gotten used to the idea. In fact, he was in high spirits and Karen was impelled to say, as they sat at their table drinking cocktails before dinner, 'Is the play going well, Clint?'

'Exceptionally well! I'm a bit stuck at the moment and so I thought we might as well have an evening out.' His smile was meant to be infectious but she ignored it.

'How long will it be before it's finished?' Her voice was cool, and she lifted a hand languorously to smother a yawn.

'I can't say, but certainly it will take less time than I estimated at first.'

'And what shall you do then?' she queried indifferently.

He frowned at her without answering.

'You're not the same, Karen,' he accused, his eyes stony and searching. 'Is something wrong?'

'I suppose I'm a little tired. I was out late last night, dancing.'

'Dancing? Who with?'

'Oh, a bloke I met in the hotel. Can I have another drink, Clint?'

'Yes. . . .' His mouth was taut, his jaw flexed. He beckoned to a passing waiter and ordered her drink.

'This man you were dancing with,' he began. 'You say you were out late?'

Karen lifted her brows in a little arrogant gesture.

'Yes, I was out late? Are there any more questions?'

'Karen,' he exploded. 'What the devil's gotten into you?'

I'm providing you with copy, she said, but silently. I'm ruining all your concepts about your heroine—and I hope I ruin the whole play while I'm about it!

Aloud she said, 'Take no notice, Clint, as I've said, I'm tired.'

'I can't help but take notice,' he returned with increasing impatience. 'It's not you—something's happened and I demand to know what it is.'

Was she going too fast? It would seem so. If she went on like this he was apt to get up and walk out on her, despite his desire to get copy.

'I'm sorry, Clint.' She gave him a winning smile. 'Forgive me. I didn't mean to be pettish.'

During dinner her manner alternated between

charm and boredom. She criticised the band, the limbo dancers and even the table service. Clint, his expression betraying his exasperation, now and then gave her the kind of look that plainly said he would like to shake her. She not only had him completely baffled, but to her intense gratification she had him gradually losing faith in her, which meant that his play would suffer.

'Shall we go?' he said tautly as soon as the meal was over.

'Go?' she pouted. 'Aren't you taking me dancing?'

'No, Karen,' he replied. 'I am not!'

She shrugged indifferently.

'You're in a strange mood tonight,' she complained.

'*I'm* in a strange mood!' he ejaculated, the cold glitter of anger in his eyes.

'Yes, just look how you are with me at this moment. We're still almost strangers, remember, so please don't begin quarreling with me as if we'd been married for years!' A hard, unmusical tone had entered her voice, not the result of anger or indignation, but caused by the pain in her heart that a situation like this had come about between Clint and herself.

'Strangers, are we?' grittingly and with dark fury creasing his brow. 'So that's how you regard us?'

'Ships that pass in the night, remember?' She smiled sweetly at him. 'You agreed with me.'

'I believe I did.' His whole manner had changed and it was pride that edged his voice. Apparently he had taken enough. He had tried hard though, having been quietly patient for most of the time, attempting to soothe away her fractiousness. And once he even asked if she were feeling off-colour, though the anxiety in his voice was obviously assumed; Karen had no doubts at all about that.

The journey back to the apartment was a silent one for the most part, both Karen and Clint being deep in thought. She felt drained because the evening had been an exhausting experience, because her acting this time affected her personally. Her heart seemed to wrench from its moorings every time Clint had looked sharply at her, and yet doggedly she had continued, to the end of the act. No, it was not quite the end. That would be when they parted at the door of the apartment. A shudder ripped through her as if an icy wind had touched her naked body. To say goodbye like this. . . . And tomorrow . . . how was she to go into that saloon on the boat and give him his breakfast without betraying any sign of emotion?

She would be glad when she had finished with him altogether, and now wished she had not bothered to give him any notice at all but had said she was leaving and just walked out on him. A man as heartless as he deserved no better treatment.

The taxi took them to the front of the hotel, where they alighted and she said he need not trouble to come to the apartment with her.

'I'll see you to your door,' he said curtly, and in silence they went through the lovely gardens toward the apartment.

'Good night,' began Karen as she put the key into the door.

He waited until the door was open and she had turned to face him, having snapped on the light, so that it lit up the room behind her.

'I intend to find out what's happened to bring about this change in you.' His voice, imperious and arrogant, had the immediate effect of making her bristle. So he was still trying, was he?—trying to get the copy that would enable him to have a few more highly successful days on the play!

'I'm far too tired to talk, Clint.'

'Tired or not, you'll talk,' he said deliberately.

Her eyes blazed.

'Who do you think you are, speaking to me like this! I haven't the slightest intention of talking. There isn't anything for us to talk about.'

'There's plenty,' he insisted steadily. 'Up till now you've been so very different from any other girl I've known, but tonight—'

'I'm not in any way different,' she broke in to deny. 'All modern girls are the same—when you've seen one you've seen the lot.'

Silence, electric and profound. Karen knew she had taken a daring chance in repeating words that had come from his own lips, spoken to his housekeeper, but she could not resist it.

'What,' he demanded tightly, 'made you say a thing like that?'

'It's true,' she replied, lifting a hand to stifle a yawn. 'I really must ask you to go, Clint. As I told you, I was out very late last night—'

'Yes,' he gritted, 'you've told me!'

She gave a deep sigh.

'You know, Clint,' she frowned, 'you accuse me of being unpredictable, but you're equally unpredictable. I should hate to be married to anyone like you. Good night,' she said again, 'I'll see you sometime—'

'By God, you won't shut me out!' His foot was in the door; it was pushed inward, forcing Karen back. She saw and heard the door slam shut, held her breath as Clint moved purposefully toward her. 'Now,' he snapped, his inclement gaze holding her eyes. 'I'll have an explanation!'

'I don't care for your manner, Clint,' she said, adopting an air of injured innocence. 'Please go—'

'What's caused this damned change?' he thundered. 'There must be some reason for it!'

'You're having a bad time, aren't you, Clint? What with your Girl Friday leaving you, and now your being repulsed by me.' She gave a light laugh. She was acting a part, one that she had acted about a month before in the production of *One Stolen Hour*.

'Repulsed, eh?' He stared at her calculatingly and then there was a sudden dramatic change as all his anger evaporated and he stood looking down at her, a reproachful expression on his lean dark face. 'Karen, what *is* the matter with you? You've changed—you're not the same girl I took out last Saturday.'

'Will you please go?' She toyed with the sequins on her evening bag, appearing to be bored and therefore finding something to do with her fingers.

Clint's teeth gritted together at the action.

'I know I said you were unpredictable, but I never expected you to be this unpredictable!' he snapped.

No . . . his heroine was letting him down badly. He would not be enjoying his writing, that was for sure. And on recalling his words about scrapping a play if he wasn't enjoying it, she was vindictive enough to hope that *Stardust and Dreams* would be scrapped.

'Are you angry because I won't let you demonstrate

your particular kind of love making?' she inquired, inserting a sneer into her voice.

'I don't care for your turn of phrase,' he objected. 'I thought we were different!' The reproach in his voice arrested her attention and she stared, half believing he was genuine after all. There was certainly a dull, hopeless sort of expression in his eyes. But the next moment they had hardened and the impression passed, and with it her doubts. He *was* acting—and making an excellent business of it, as he had done from the first.

'From what?' archly as she moved away, toward the window at the far side of the room from where he was standing. 'Why should we be different? I said we're as ships that pass in the night. We had a flirtation and it was nice while it lasted but it's over—'

'Stop it!' he thundered, advancing toward her. 'What the devil are you up to?'

She laughed, a harshness in her voice resulting from the effort she was making to hold back the cloud of bitter tears that had gathered behind her eyes.

'It's the truth. I mean—no one bothers about love these days, do they? Life's for living, and tomorrow you'll probably have someone else and so will I.'

'So that's it. . . . My God,' he spat out contemptuously, 'you were right! You're no different from the rest!' He stood looking at her, and suddenly she had the incredible impression that, mingling with the shades of harshness in his eyes there was a sort of vacant glaze of bitterness and disillusionment which caused her heart to contract. Was it possible that she had made a mistake? Did he love her? With a little intake of breath she was about to speak, to ask him outright if he cared, but the impulse was stemmed almost immediately by a logical recognition of fact as her eyes focused the picture she had seen through that archway in the restaurant in Bridgetown—Clint and his girl friend. Having told Karen he could not see her for a few days as he would be working hard on his play, he yet had the time to take another girl out to lunch.

Determinedly Karen hardened her heart, producing a laugh as she said archly, 'I must say, Clint, that *you* are a little different from the rest in that you've a certain finesse which I've never come across before. I did enjoy our little—er—affair, even though it's finished now.'

'Finished, is it?' The vibration in his voice was like the guttural warning of a jungle cat about to attack. She saw his fine nostrils quiver as crimson threads of fury crept up the sides of his mouth, discolouring the dark tan of his skin, and a tremor of uneasiness went through her. Apprehensively she wondered if she had carried the farce beyond the limit of what he could take. He looked ready to murder her, she thought, his vicious fury filling the very air around them. 'Be careful,' he snarled. 'You know very little about me. I can punish, so don't flaunt your promiscuity in my face. As for its being finished—that'll be when *I* say so!'

She was really frightened now, her voice quivering and frayed as she asked him to leave.

'I shall leave when I'm ready.' So soft the tone, like the whispered threat of a predator about to take its prey. Without being conscious of what she was doing Karen dropped her evening bag on to a chair and backed away, a trembling sensation in her knees. Endless moments dragged by before he said, in the same dangerously quiet tone of voice, 'Come here.' He was pointing arrogantly to a spot on the floor right in front of him. Instead of obeying Karen moved further from him, as far as she could before she felt the window sill touch her back. Her heartbeats became erratic, painful against her ribs, her nerves were knotted by fear. Why had she goaded him this far?—to the actual point of physical attack?

'Please go—please don't hurt me—' A harsh and ruthless laugh slashed through her faltering plea and a shattering weakness began to spread through her body when he repeated his command for her to come to him.

'No! I—you're trespassing! You haven't any right to be here—' She got no further, every vestige of colour draining from her as, with the spring of a tiger on the attack he covered the distance between them, and before she had time to move, her wrist was caught in a vice-like grip and her protesting body jerked ruthlessly to the whipcord hardness of his. An arrogant hand beneath her chin brought her head up so that his sensuous mouth could crush hers in brutal, dominating savagery. Desperately she struggled, terror lending her strength to kick out at his shins as she had done once before but this time she was mercilessly shaken, a cry of protest escaping her as her tongue was caught between her teeth.

'Let me go, you fiend!' she cried. 'I'll have the police on you if—' The rest was smothered by his kiss but once more she began to struggle, managing to drag her mouth from his. He caught a handful of hair, jerking her head right back, and another cry issued from her lips as the pain in her neck seemed to shoot right down into her chest.

'So it's finished, is it?' he snarled, holding on to her hair, compelling her to look up into his eyes. White to the lips, she was drowned in a deluge of terror that threatened to deprive her of her senses as she saw the smouldering embers of primitive need in his expression. She was lost, she thought, her heart pounding so madly that she felt physically sick. The agony was still in her neck and she dared not move; she closed her eyes to the approach of his mouth, giving a stifled moan as it cruelly bruised her lips. His tongue with thrusting arrogance touched the roughness of hers. She was a captive in his arms, utterly helpless against his strength and, to her shame, vulnerable to his masculine enticement. For even his cruelty drew her, his magnetism far too strong for her feeble efforts at resistance. Rapture flooded her whole being even though she winced at the steel of his hand when it found its way inside her bodice and the lean brown fingers took masterful possession of her breasts. And when his other hand forced her slender frame against the throbbing hardness of his loins she found herself swept irresistibly into the maelstrom of an all-consuming passion equal to his own, and for long moments she swayed dizzily to a tempestuous rhythm that spread rapture into every nerve and cell in her body.

At last, breathing heavily, he held her from him, a sneering lift of triumph to his mouth as he saw the dark and dreamy glaze that covered her eyes. His gaze settled on her heaving breasts for a moment, before seeming to become fascinated by the rhythmic rise and fall of her stomach.

'Well, Karen,' he said in some amusement, 'it wasn't finished, was it? But it is now, because *I* say so. You're free of me from this moment on.' And without another word he swung away from her and left the room, closing the door quietly behind him.

Chapter Nine

Helen was still out when Karen returned to the bungalow, and a feeling of immeasurable relief swept over her. Helen knew of the date with Clint and would naturally want to know all about it but Karen was in no mood for answering questions that could only be an embarrassment, revealing in all its stark truth the merciless retaliation of the man she still loved. With shadowed eyes still swollen by tears she glanced down at the angry bruise on her wrist. That one was visible but she wondered how many others he had inflicted on her body. Never in her wildest dreams could she have visualised the sheer unbridled savagery to which Clint had subjected her. Listlessly she went to the tiny room in which there was a bed, wardrobe, small dressing table and a chair. Helen was occupying the airy, well-furnished room that was Jean's and although when Karen informed her she would be sleeping at the bungalow Helen had naturally offered her the better room, Karen would not hear of her relinquishing it.

She sank down on the bed, fully expecting sleep to elude her, and wishing with all her heart that she didn't have to go to the boat tomorrow and face the man who had treated her so ruthlessly.

What a revelation his behaviour had been! And yet, it was reminiscent of that first encounter on the grounds of Sam Lord's Castle. But, strangely, through it all Karen had been aware of a nebulous sense of perplexity which she found it impossible to grasp.

The silence of the tiny room was heavy and depressing after she had gotten into bed, to lie awake, staring into the dimness, seeing nothing.

She still loved Clint with passionate intensity, so how was she to get over it? She was philosophical enough to accept that the pain would fade with time, but in no way could she visualise having anyone else. Clint was her ideal, a god in her eyes, and no other man could ever come anywhere near his perfection.

She would never be able to settle for second best.

The following morning she rose very early, with the deliberate intention of delaying her meeting with Helen, and by half-past five Karen was in her disguise and on her way to the boat. She would spend the extra hours in polishing the furniture and cleaning the windows. And she might as well do some packing and bring away most of what few things were still on the boat, consisting mainly of her housekeeper's clothes.

To her surprise and dismay Clint was already up, and his eyes widened on seeing her arrive so early.

'Do you usually come at this time?' he asked.

'No, but I want to clean the windows, and do some polishing. It'll then last for a while—until you get someone else to take my place.'

He was on deck, his face drawn, his eyes faintly protuberant as if he had been staring through them for unrelieved hours of concentration. Pain touched Karen's heart even while she admonished herself for feeling any sort of sympathy for him. It was all so very plain as to the reason for his haggard appearance. His play had gone wrong because of the unexpected behaviour of his heroine, and so he hadn't slept. Well, that was what she had wanted—for him to ruin it, and vindictively she hoped that he would scrap it in the end. Stardust and dreams. . . . That had been her definition of romance when asked for it, and that was exactly what her brief romance with Clint had been. Stardust and dreams . . . abstract, fading with the dawning enlightenment that he had ruthlessly used her for his own ends—for his own glory and financial gain, in fact. Playing with her, pretending to love her . . . making love to her. Well, his triumph, like her happiness, had been short-lived. The play could never be what he had planned, and she was very sure that the famous Clint Fraser would never produce anything mediocre, for if he did then his reputation would suffer.

'You needn't trouble,' he said broodingly. 'I shall not be staying here after tomorrow. I'm returning to my home, so you must have all your belongings off the boat sometime today.'

'Your play, Mr. Fraser,' she began, marveling at the steadiness of her voice, 'is it not going well? Is that why you're leaving?'

'It's not going well,' he answered tautly, looking through her rather than at her. 'In fact, I shall never finish it now.'

'Not finish it?' with well-assumed concern. 'But surely, after all the work—'

'The work's unimportant,' he broke in irritably. 'Perfection was my aim, and this play can never be perfect now.'

'But what will you do with it?' she asked, because she really wanted to be sure that he meant to scrap it.

'Throw it away.' The bitterness in his voice brought a quality of harshness with it and Karen, swallowing hard, was on the verge of feeling sorry for him when a sharp stab of recollection brought back the picture of him and his girl friend lunching in the restaurant in Bridgetown.

'I'm sorry to hear that,' she said speciously. 'You've been several weeks on it and it seems such a waste.'

'You'll pack your things this morning?' he asked, ignoring her sympathetic comment. 'You can go when you like.'

'But your dinner tonight?' It was ridiculous, but now that the actual parting from him was at hand, she wanted to stay, to look after him. 'I can come back to do that, surely?'

He was already shaking his head, and there was a sort of dejected tiredness about him as he said, 'I don't need you to do that. I'm dining out this evening.'

Dining out . . . with his girl friend? Yes, Karen was sure of it and the knowledge was a knife turning in her heart.

A few minutes later he came to her, an envelope in his hand.

'Here's your money,' he said. 'I'm paying you to the end of the month.' Karen opened her mouth to object but he gave her no time as he went on, 'It so happens that you gave me your notice,' he said, 'but as things have turned out I'd have been asking you to go anyway, in which case I'd have been obliged to pay you the full six months' money—'

'No, you wouldn't,' she broke in, then stopped as his mouth compressed in anger.

'Take this!' The envelope was thrust at her so that she had no alternative than to take it. 'I probably shan't see you again as I've work to do in my study and I shall be there for a couple of hours or so. There's money for your fare back to England—no,' he said sternly, 'don't interrupt. I brought you here and it's incumbent on me to pay your fare back.'

Karen had finished packing and was ready to leave but she stayed in her cabin, undecided about saying goodbye to Clint, who had been closeted in his study since breakfast time, not making a sound. And without the familiar rhythmic sound of the typewriter the boat seemed dead. Gloomily Karen looked at the suitcase that lay on the bed—the other having been taken to Jean's bungalow weeks ago with Karen's "younger" clothes—and a shuddering sigh that was almost a sob escaped her. This really was the momentous and heartbreaking end to an escapade that should never have taken place. Clint had lost his play and she her heart.

Her ears suddenly became alert as she realised that Clint had come from his study.

Karen emerged from the cabin, her suitcase in her hand.

'I'll say goodbye, Mr. Fraser.' Her eyes fell to the large, polyethylene bag he carried. It was full of clean papers . . . the manuscript. Where was he taking it? She wondered.

'Goodbye, Miss Waring. Have a safe flight home.' Swinging on his heel, he left her there, the lone occupant of the boat. Tears rose easily but she dared not let them fall, not with all this paint on her face. Slowly she followed as soon as he was down the gangplank. She kept him in sight as he strode away toward the Smuggler's Cove Hotel, her brows creasing in a frown as her curiosity increased. He was walking quickly; she hurried to keep him in view, and just as she reached the place where she could enter the grounds of the Vervain Hotel she realized with a little thumping sensation in her heart that Clint was on his way to the back of the Smuggler's Cove Hotel where the refuse was put in readiness to be collected. She stopped in the shelter of some bushes, waiting for him to come back, which he did—without the bag.

Something within her seemed to snap; she knew it wasn't logical—indeed it was highly illogical—but the thought of the manuscript being carried away with the hotel refuse was so painful that she wanted to cry. And yet she had worked and schemed for just this!

'I'm glad it's gone!' she whispered fiercely . . . but knew she was not glad at all.

Helen had told Karen yesterday that as it was Roger's afternoon off today she and he were taking a trip to Welshman's Gully, and so Karen had the bungalow to herself as she thankfully got rid of her disguise and began to unpack her suitcase. But insistently the nagging picture of the manuscript being destroyed was on her mind. The tremendous effort Clint had put into the play, the eagerness with which he had spoken about it, the very likely possibility that one day in the future he might be able to finish it . . . all these conjoined to spur Karen's thoughts to an action, the result of which she could not at the moment visualise. She had no idea what she would do with the manuscript, but the urgent matter of the moment was to rescue it before the collection truck arrived, which it did every day about this time, and without any more time being lost in reasoning she dashed out, hurrying across the wide lawns and gardens of the Vervain Hotel and onto the grounds of the Smuggler's Cove where she made for the back of the low, spreading building. It seemed an eternity before she got there, and when she did, she stopped, breathless, to stare in dismay at the activity going on.

The rubbish was all contained in huge bins placed against one wall, and it was plain that most of them had already had their contents emptied into the truck, whose churning mechanism was effectively reducing them to pulp.

'Wait!' cried Karen on seeing two men lift what appeared to be the last of the bins, as all the others were back in their neat positions against the wall. 'I've lost something!' She ran on, waving a hand and to her relief the men stopped to stare at her. 'Something was thrown away by mistake,' she gasped on reaching them. 'May I look inside the bin before you empty it?'

'You can, miss,' agreed one of the men who belonged to the hotel staff, 'but was it in this one? All the others have been emptied.'

'It might be in that one,' she began, then stopped. There were eight large bins in all so the chances of it being in the last one seemed very remote indeed. However, she asked the man to remove the lid . . . and she couldn't believe her eyes when she saw, lying on top of a pile of clean newspapers, the polyethylene bag containing Clint's manuscript.

'That's it!' Thankfully she accepted it from the man when he lifted it out for her.

'It looks important,' he remarked, obviously wondering how anything of that size had been put accidentally into the bin.

'It is important. Thank you very much for your help.'

'That's okay, miss. I'm glad you got it.' He was still looking puzzled but Karen just smiled at him and moved away.

But now that the manuscript that had caused her such heartache was safely in her hands she wondered what she would do with it ultimately. Perhaps, she thought, she would one day post it to Clint, anonymously. Of course he would know that the rescuer could be none other than Miss Waring, but that was all. His curiosity as to her reason would never be satisfied.

Her action had at the time seemed to have been purely instinctive, inspired by her love for Clint and nothing more. But now she knew there had been some other spur as well, knew without any doubt at all that if she had left the manuscript there she would never have been able to get it out of her mind. Perhaps it was the fact that she had always deplored waste of any kind, and to have allowed the destruction of a manuscript that was almost finished would have been a waste both of Clint's time and his inspiration.

Yes, she was glad she had rescued it, she decided, and after putting it away in one of the drawers in her bedroom she settled down with a magazine. But the effort to concentrate was too much and she decided to wash her hair. The shampoo she used was expensive but it always left her hair gleaming and scented with the fragrance clinging for a full day even if she got her hair wet again when it had dried. After toweling it vigourously she went out to the patio to let it dry in the fresh air of the hotel gardens. She sat in a lounge contemplating the immediate scene of exotic flowers flaunting perfume and colour, of bikini-clad figures on the nearby beach and of surf riders on the shimmering, aquamarine sea. Along one side of the extensive grounds, and at right angles to the silver shore, magnificent dome palms speared the metallic blue of the Caribbean sky. Insects murmuring in the hibiscus bushes, humming birds in the poinciana trees; a pink and green lizard rigidly still against the amphora-shaped earthenware vase where flourished a bougainvillea vine that had spread right up the wall of the bungalow and across the top of the living room window . . . all this would have been magic to Karen a few days ago.

Naturally as she sat there her thoughts were on the manuscript she had rescued, and gradually it was borne on her that she had no right to have it in her possession. It was not her property and, in effect, she had taken it unlawfully. Her nerves jerked when she thought of what Clint might say if he knew what she had done, and that the work he definitely meant to be destroyed had been rescued and was in someone else's possession. The more she dwelt on it the more doubtful she became as to the wisdom of her action, one that was as impulsive as that which had precipitated her into the vast web of deceit from which she had escaped only at a cost so dear that it would be years before she recovered.

Serious qualms assailed her, causing her heartbeats to quicken. Perhaps it was her general state of mind that made it appear almost a felony for her to have Clint's manuscript in her possession. She'd no right to it, and as the disturbing moments passed she felt she would have to get rid of it, to take it back—But, no! It was unthinkable that she should put it into one of those bins, to be taken away tomorrow. Another, more acceptable idea flashed into her mind and, rising, she went inside to assume the disguise which she had believed she would never use again.

She would have liked to run to the boat right away with the manuscript but although she suspected that Clint would not be on it she could not be absolutely sure, so it was far too risky to go as she was, for the last thing she wanted now was to let him know of the masquerade! He would murder her, she thought, recalling with a convulsive shudder what she had already suffered at his hands.

With the greasepaint applied, she donned the same dress she had worn that morning and then, after hastily crushing her newly washed hair beneath the wig, she put the polyethylene bag containing the manuscript into a canvas shopping bag and hurried from the bungalow, not bothering to lock the door. She had gone through the grounds of both hotels when she turned, heart leaping, as she heard footsteps behind her. Mr. Lawson! Anger lit her eyes even before he said,

'Can I walk with you? I'll carry your bag if you like—?'

'No, you can't. I'm sorry—and I'm in a hurry!' In order to get away from him she forgot all about her disguise and started to run, and only when she had left him well behind did she resume the sedate pace she always used when approaching the boat, just in case Clint should be some place where he could see her. She hurried through the path to find that the old man was nowhere in sight.

If Clint should be on the boat she had an excuse ready: she had forgotten something. But as she saw no movement, no figure on that part of the deck which was visible to her, she walked resolutely up the gangplank and sped along to the cabin she had used. Kneeling down, she lifted the lid of a low bunk and dropped the manuscript inside, wincing as, closing the lid, its corner scraped her head. One day the manuscript would be found, and Clint might just finish it—Her thoughts were cut as she heard a step on the deck. So Clint was still on board. Her heart began to beat rapidly at the prospect of having to face him again, so she waited, hoping he might just be leaving the boat, but he seemed to be pacing about so she decided to get it over and done with and, opening the door of the cabin, she stepped out into the narrow corridor, and walked along it to the deck.

'Miss Waring . . . I saw you running. Is anything wrong?'

'You—s-saw m-me running?' she repeated tremulously.

'Yes, and very spritely you were too.'

'It was that old man,' she offered, 'he was making a nuisance of himself again.'

'I see. Why have you come back?'

'I left something behind—my brooch.'

'And you have it now?'

'Yes—thank you.' He was looking oddly at her, the concentrated intentness of his gaze alerting her to the fact that something had captured his eyes. Automatically she fluttered a hand to the place focused, and to her horror touched the silken softness of her own dark hair! When the lid of the bunk scraped her head her wig must have moved slightly. Paralysed for a micron of time, during which there was the fear of brutal treatment, she turned, fleeing to the gangplank. But the deck was slightly wet from the few drops of rain that had fallen while she was in the cabin and her legs shot out from under her. She knew a fierce, blinding stab of agony before she fell into the water.

She awoke to the instant knowledge of what had happened, and to the physical sensations of dizziness and nausea, with the awareness of a dull ache at her temple. But soon the dizziness and nausea passed and she sat up. She was in her cabin, lying on the bunk bed with a cool white sheet covering her nakedness.

Burning colour stole into her cheeks as her brain registered the fact that Clint must have stripped her of her wet clothing.

Clint knew everything now and fear rose to vanquish her embarrassment as she wondered what sort of punishment he would inflict on her this time. Everything had gone wrong! She could have wept, but instead she sat up, thankful to know that apart from the ache in her temple she appeared to be none the worse for her experience. She slid from the bed, wrapping the sheet tightly around her. No sound. But she could not get off the boat without her clothes.

Well, this was the showdown—and how very different from what she had planned! Hers was to have been the laugh while Clint was to eat his words of criticism of her acting.

Her eyes dilated as the door opened quietly and Clint stood there, stern and frighteningly dark. She swallowed, trying to remove the constriction in her throat. Was she to receive similar treatment to that which she had already tasted? There would be little hope of escape dressed as she was in nothing but a sheet which she must assuredly lose if it became necessary to struggle with him again. What a mess to be in!—at the mercy of the man who, judging by his expression, was having the greatest difficulty in repressing his anger.

Endless moments passed before he spoke and when he did it was to ask prosaically, 'How do you feel? Is your head aching?'

'Just a little,' she answered in a low tone of voice.

'Any other aches or pains?' He came into the cabin

as he spoke, closing the door behind him—an ominous move it seemed to Karen whose fretted nerve-ends were playing up.

'No—I haven't anything else wrong with me. Thank you for bringing me out of the water.' She stared at him and it did seem that the fury in his eyes evaporated somewhat on seeing that she was practically none the worse for her experience.

'Well, Karen,' he said, tautly. 'Perhaps you will tell me what this is all about?'

She nodded immediately, deciding that the best policy under the circumstances was to make a full confession, leaving nothing out, humiliating though it would be to her to admit that she loved him. Rather that, though, than come in for another of his brutal attacks during which her scanty covering would undoubtedly come away.

'I did it to be revenged on you, Clint,' she faltered, sitting down on her bed and drawing the sheet more tightly around her. 'As you thought, I did hear your disparaging comments on my acting, and I was piqued. At that time my boss had left and I wanted a job. I knew the advertisement was yours; the prospect of getting the job was attractive in that I'd make you eat your words about my acting, and also it enabled me to be near my sister.' She stopped, staring wanly at him. 'I didn't realise what would be the outcome of it all. It was a mischievous act,' she quivered, tears on her lashes, 'but certainly not a wicked one. However, it—it served me right that I—I f-fell in love with you—'

'You—' he broke off and it seemed for a moment as if

nothing would have given him greater satisfaction than to strangle her. 'There's more, obviously,' he rasped. 'Carry on! It's an interesting story. I want to hear the rest of it!'

'I believed, like a fool,' she added bitterly, 'that you returned my love but I soon realised what your little game was, and that you were putting on an act, only pretending to love me so that you could use me for your own ends.'

Clint seemed to be practising infinite restraint.

'And what,' he demanded through his teeth, 'was my little game, as you term it?'

'You were merely using me for copy—Oh, yes, you were,' she went on hurriedly when it seemed he would open his mouth. 'Don't forget that I saw two sides of you. You told your housekeeper that your heroine wasn't satisfactory, that you wanted her to be unusual, unpredictable. Well, that was how you described me, Karen, but I didn't catch on at first. I was unpredictable in your eyes because of what had happened that first night at Sam Lord's Castle. Well, I flirted with you just for a joke, because I knew who you were, remember; I had the advantage of you. And it was because you'd said such horrid things about my acting that I tried to flirt with you—just to be able to remind you, later, when the job on the boat folded up, that I *could* act.' She paused, mainly for breath because her words had been heated and spoken swiftly and for the most part with indignation.

'Do continue,' Clint encouraged steadily, and he stepped back to lean against one corner of the wardrobe, his hands folded across his chest. 'I rather think,' he added sarcastically, 'that *you* ought to be writing plays.'

Her eyes flew to his, for something about his manner brought feathery tingles of doubt—and apprehension—to her spine. However, she carried on, 'As your housekeeper I several times asked you about the play, and learned that it went right only after you'd seen me—not your housekeeper—after you'd been out with Karen. . . .' She trailed off, her colour rising at the hint of amusement that had entered his eyes. But it had no softening effect; they were still as hard as granite.

'Do tell me more,' he invited patiently, and made himself more comfortable as if expecting the story to be a long one.

Falteringly she said, 'I don't understand your attitude, Clint?'

'You will,' grittingly, 'in just a few moments.'

Startled, she grasped the sheet more firmly around her, wondering if she imagined it or if there really was a threat in his tone.

'Well, as I couldn't very well condemn you out of hand—'

'You couldn't? That was generous.'

Karen averted her head at his cold sarcasm and tried to keep her voice steady as she continued, 'And so I decided to take a look at your manuscript, which I had never done before, and the first thing I noticed was the title. It was right at the top of the page.'

'It usually is,' with the same icy sarcasm, and her colour deepened. She was feeling decidedly uncomfortable and if it weren't that she was so scared she could have told him to go to the devil; she wasn't telling him any more. But she *was* scared—very, alone with him in this tiny cabin and clad only in a sheet which, if he should choose, could be whipped off her with one swift movement of those lean brown fingers.

'*Stardust and Dreams*. . . .' Her lips began to quiver so she spoke swiftly, hoping he had not noticed. 'You stole my title—'

'*Your* title?' with a lift of an eyebrow. 'Why, are you writing something?'

At that her eyes did sparkle and, forgetting her fear for an instant she said recklessly, 'Don't be so damned sarcastic with me! I'm telling you what you want to know but if you go on like this I shan't speak at all!'

His response was a significant raking of her body and a very quiet warning for her to take care as she was in a most vulnerable situation.

'Carry on,' he ordered in the same soft voice, 'I'm determined to hear the whole idiotic story.'

'Idiotic?'

'Carry on,' he prompted. 'My manner's deceptive. My patience is almost exhausted. The way I feel at present I could strip that thing from your back and give you something that would make you smart for a month.'

Vivid colour stained her cheeks and instinctively she clutched the sheet between tightly closed fists.

'I was saying that, as Miss Waring, I could look at the manuscript and I very soon discovered that my suspicions were correct. You *had* been using me, and so I decided to give you copy all right—the kind that would ruin your play altogether. Your heroine was more unpredictable than you could ever have visualised, wasn't she?' For some reason she could not explain, Karen was gathering courage, and she added triumphantly, 'I was cleverer than you, Clint! Your acting isn't half as good as mine! In fact, you weren't very clever at all, really, because I saw through you!'

'So I wasn't very clever, eh? But you were?'

'Yes, I was! I saw through your falseness!'

At that his eyebrows lifted a fraction.

'You?—daring to mention falseness?' he said, for the moment diverted.

She had the grace to blush but her chin lifted all the same.

'My deceit was done for a joke more than anything else; yours was sheer rottenness!'

The gray eyes glinted dangerously but Karen failed to notice as, the sheet having slipped a little, she was busy bringing it up to her chin again.

'How much of the manuscript did you read?' asked Clint curiously.

'Not much, but enough. The last few pages you'd written told me all I needed to know. . . .' Her voice trailed as he took a step that brought him closer to her. Involuntarily she got off the bed and stepped back, her heart fluttering uncomfortably, as if she had something alive inside her.

'And from those few passages you gained all the proof you needed to make you put on that act?'

'Yes. I gave you plenty of copy—and I ruined the play, didn't I?'

'Oh, yes, you made an excellent job of that.' He was

coming closer but Karen was unable to retreat any further because the backs of her legs were touching the bed. 'It's finished—scrapped!' He was towering over her now, a menacing figure, big and powerful and very frightening.

The colour drained from Karen's face and her voice was strained to huskiness as she quavered, 'Don't you dare touch me. I'll scream—' She cut her words raggedly as Clint, his fury breaking the bonds that had been controlling it, grabbed her roughly, jerking her toward him.

'You'd scream, would you?' he gritted. 'Then let me give you something to scream for!' His fingers were steel as they fastened on her shoulders, and he shook her until he himself was breathless.

'Do you know what you've done?' he thundered, his face twisted with fury. 'You're so clever, did you say? My God, girl, I ought to beat you for your cleverness!' Wrathfully he flung her from him but made sure she fell on to the bed. The sheet came open and she clutched it to her again, every nerve in her body rioting.

'I hate you,' she seethed.

'Then that makes two of us! You've made me act like a brute!' Although there was wrath in his voice, Karen somehow gained the impression that he was not now quite as angry as before, and the tautness of her nerves slackened a little.

'Can I help if it you've a violent nature?'

'I haven't a violent nature!' he denied explosively, and in the next breath he was adding, 'I could strangle you, slowly, for what you've done!'

'And you say you haven't a violent nature?'

He gritted his teeth and cast her a smouldering glance.

'All that work—for nothing. The best thing I've ever written! Gone—destroyed!'

'The best thing?' she repeated slowly, her eyes searching his face. 'How can it be, when you haven't got the right ending?'

'But I have! Although *you* don't know it!'

'You have?' Bewilderedly she felt that his words ought to have conveyed something of vital importance to her but her mind was dazed, her nerves chaotic, and so clear thinking was difficult. 'I don't understand, Clint,' she added in a tremulous little voice.

'You will—one day!' he rasped. 'If I don't kill you beforehand!'

Now, she thought, was the time to tell him the play was safe, but instead, she started to cry, the result of overwrought nerves and the sick feeling within her because of the shaking she'd received.

'What the devil's wrong with you now?' he demanded heartlessly.

'I w-want my—my clothes—'

'They're wet!'

'I expect they are,' she gulped. 'How—c-can I get some more?'

'I suppose I shall have to get them for you, from the bungalow.'

'I'd be grateful. Helen's out but the door isn't locked. My room's the one at the back, the tiny one—' She broke off, colouring. 'If you'd please bring my beach shorts and top—they're drying on the patio—'

'Don't put on another act with me,' he advised. 'I couldn't stand it! The modest miss, eh? I've just stripped you, remember?'

'No, I don't remember, because I was unconscious!'

Clint drew an exasperated breath and let it out slowly, as if the exercise would give him some sort of control.

She looked up into his face, and in one fleeting second of time his expression changed and she just happened to catch it. A great surge of emotion rose up from somewhere near her heart, settling in her chest to make breathing difficult. A trembling hand stole to her cheek.

'I think—think I've m-made a m-mistake. . . .'

'*A* mistake?' he barked. 'You've made half a dozen! This disgusting and deceitful masquerade, for one thing—'

'You'd never have written your play if I hadn't come to you as Miss Waring, because you'd never have met me—Karen—the girl you wanted to use!'

'The play *would* have been written,' he corrected, 'but differently! I came here specifically to write the play!'

'Well, that might be so, but later you changed it, because you didn't know how to handle your heroine.'

'Didn't I?' Soft the voice and dangerous. 'Well, I know how to handle her now!' and before Karen could grasp his meaning he had taken her in his arms and for several excruciating moments she knew once again the savagery of his hard demanding mouth.

He released her at last and stood looking down into her face.

'Clint,' she faltered, lifting a hand as if in entreaty,

'you mentioned your—your heroine—and then you kissed m-me. And just now you said you had the right ending—'

'The right ending,' he broke in and now his words were bitter, 'but no play!'

'Clint—I—the play is—'

'If you'd read a bit more, your malicious misinterpretations of my motives would never have occurred!'

'Wh-what part, Clint?' The tears were sparkling on her lashes again but in her heart there was joy, for in spite of the dark anger and bitterness on Clint's face she knew without any doubt at all that he loved her. 'You see—'

'Pages one hundred and ten and one hundred and thirty-six!—but it's too late now!' He strode to the door. 'I'll get your clothes,' he said and was gone.

Pages one hundred and ten and one hundred and thirty-six. . . . No sooner had the door slammed, its vibration shaking the cabin, than Karen was down on her knees, opening the bunk and lifting out the manuscript. With feverish haste she found page one hundred and ten. Written lightly in pencil on the wide margin were the words, 'It was at this point that I realised that although I was getting copy from Karen, I had fallen in love with her.' For a long while Karen could only stare, her mind a tangle of unconnected thoughts. If only she had gone back a little instead of reading the last part. Swallowing convulsively she flicked over the next pages to read one hundred and thirty-six. Another handwritten note was in the wide margin. 'It was hard not to make a date but I must get this finished with all possible speed. We can then be married and have a prolonged honeymoon cruising the Caribbean.'

It seemed an eternity before she heard Clint coming along the passage and stopping outside the door. Her heart was full, her eyes shining with happiness. What a wonderful surprise he was going to get! Every nerve tingled in anticipation of her reward—his arms about her in a loving caress, his lips, tender and gentle, claiming hers.

The door swung inward; she saw the small leather case he carried, saw his eyes widen in disbelief on seeing the manuscript there, in the prominent position where she had put it, so that he would notice it immediately when he came in.

'What—?' Dropping the case on to the floor he took a couple of strides and picked up the manuscript. 'Where the devil did this come from?' He swung round to stare interrogatingly at her.

'I rescued it,' she told him happily, then went on to explain how she came to know it was with the refuse. 'But then I didn't know what to do with it, Clint, so I decided to bring it over and leave it in the bunk here, for you to find sometime in the future. I've just read the notes you'd written. But I knew you loved me before then. And,' she added simply, 'I love you. I've already told you—' She stopped, staggered by his thunderous expression. 'Aren't you glad—?'

'So it was in there all the time we were talking? Then why the hell didn't you say so! I've been nearly out of my mind for the past hour, cursing myself for acting so foolishly, and all the time it was in there?

I've had about as much as I can take from you!' He advanced purposefully toward her. 'You're going to get—'

'Don't you dare touch me!' she cried, tears of disappointment in her eyes. 'I thought you loved me and would be glad because you—you s-said you'd gotten the—the ending—h-happy ending I th-thought—' Her words broke on a choking little sob. Clint's eyes softened miraculously but she failed to notice, '—but you don't love me and I don't love you—Oh, please go away! I want to get dressed. The sooner I'm out of here the better!'

It was less than half an hour later that Karen and Clint were standing close together on the sunlit deck of the *Fair Mermaid*, the last of the misunderstandings having been straightened out. Karen had learned that although Clint's original intention was to use her for copy—because she seemed to be the perfect example of the heroine he intended to create—he had realised, after that night at the Southern Palms Hotel, that his bachelor days were nearing their end.

'You captivated me, darling, and after we had made love so wonderfully I knew without any doubt at all that you were the girl for me.' His voice was filled with tender emotion, his eyes dark with love as, bending his head, he took her eager lips in a long, passionate kiss that instantly stimulated her emotions, quickening the blood in her veins, creating an intoxicating lightness in her body.

After a while he held her from him, tender amusement in his gaze as he saw the dreamy expression in her eyes.

'Any more questions, sweet?' he asked after a space. 'Or have we cleared everything up?'

She hesitated, and then told him she had seen him lunching with his girl friend, when he was supposed to be working hard on the play.

'I did take her to lunch, yes—' He stopped, frowning at the idea that Karen had seen him.

She smiled a little wanly and said, 'It strengthened my suspicions that I'd made a mistake in thinking you loved me.'

'It must have done. It was unfortunate that you saw us together. I decided to take her out as a final gesture and to tell her I'd met the girl I was going to marry. She took it very well,' he added. 'But it had never reached the serious stage. We got along well together and enjoyed each other's company—and the day might have come when it developed into something deeper. But after I met you. . . .' His tender gaze was fixed on Karen's lovely face, and with a little exclamation he bent his head and kissed her quivering lips. It was a gentle kiss at first, and indeed he never meant it to be anything other than gentle, but at the cloudy desire in her eyes, the tempting mouth, honey-rose and faintly moist, his ardour flared and she was swept into the vortex of his lovemaking, crushed against his virile body, her mouth possessed in a way that left her in no doubt that Clint would always be her master.

She was breathless when eventually he released her.

'Clint,' she gasped, impishly teasing, 'You're cruel! I

don't think I ought to marry you—' The rest was halted by his expression and the faint lift of an eyebrow.

'I wasn't aware that I had asked you to marry me,' he reminded her with well-feigned arrogance.

She coloured, lowering her lashes. But a moment later she tilted her chin and said,

'Well, since there's Women's Lib and all that—*I* shall propose to *you*. Will you—?' Again she was stopped, this time by a slap that was meant to hurt—and it did.

'You, my girl, can forget Women's Lib! I'm the master and I'm also old-fashioned enough to feel it's the man's prerogative to do the proposing.' He paused a moment, his eyes challengingly severe. 'If you feel you can't live with my cruelty then you only have to refuse. Will you marry me, my dearest love?' The change in his tone was dramatic, and the look in his eyes was now one of tenderness and deepest love.

Karen snuggled against the hardness of his breast, murmuring softly, 'Yes, dearest Clint, I will marry you.'

'I adore you,' he whispered close to her hair. 'I don't think I can wait until the play's finished,' he added decisively, and Karen leaned away to ask, 'Will it take long, Clint, now that you have the ending you want?'

'About a month.' The gray eyes were satirically mocking. 'Are *you* willing to wait that long, my love?' And without giving her time to answer he added, sternly, 'No putting on an act, my girl! I've had about as much of that as I can take. Your acting days are over, understand?'

She pouted.

'It's fun, Clint—a great hobby, and as I do it so well—' She broke off as he gave her a little shake.

'That's the trouble; you do it too well!—Miss Waring!'

Mischief brought a sparkle to Karen's eyes.

'Aren't you glad she decided on the masquerade?' she asked, peeping up at him from under her lashes.

Ignoring that Clint said, 'You weren't perfect in that particular role, you know. For one thing, your hands interested me. They were young hands. Then there were those absurd scraps of lace you were washing—' He broke off, amusement in his gaze.

'Helen and I had a good laugh over that,' admitted Karen, catching his humour.

'And over a good many more things, I expect?'

She nodded her head, thinking of Helen and wondering what she would have to say about all this. And Karen wondered too if Helen would eventually marry her new boy friend and come to live on Barbados. She rather thought she would.

'I asked you if you could wait a month?' Clint's voice, interrupting Karen's train of thought, was strong yet tender, and faintly masterful. Holding her from him, he looked deeply into her eyes, saw the dreamy cloud of longing and added on that same note of mocking satire, 'No, apparently you can't. We shall be married within a week.'

As Karen had no objection to this she remained contentedly silent, and after a long interlude of kissing and caressing Clint said, a laugh in his voice, 'Darling, could I ask a favour of you? I have a hunch that my housekeeper won't show up any more—that she's walked out on me, and as I'm still in a hurry to finish the play—which has a stupendous finale, as you know—would you come over each morning and "do" for me?'

A ripple of laughter escaped Karen as she replied, 'I'd love to do for you, Clint. I'm so glad Miss Waring's walked out on you.'

'And I, my dearest,' he said when he had kissed her, 'have to admit that although she caused me a great deal of trouble, I'm so very glad that she walked in on me in the first place.'

READERS' COMMENTS ON SILHOUETTE ROMANCES:

"You give us joy and surprises throughout the books . . . they're the best books I've read."

—J.S.*, Crosby, MN

"Needless to say I am addicted to your books. . . . I love the characters, the settings, the emotions."

—V.D., Plane, TX

"Every one was written with the utmost care. The story of each captures one's interest early in the plot and holds it through until the end."

—P.B., Summersville, WV

"I get so carried away with the books I forget the time."

—L.W., Beltsville, MD

"Silhouette has a great talent for picking winners."

—K.W., Detroit, MI

* names available on request.